EXAMPLES IN
C.S.E. MATHEMATICS
(METRIC EDITION)

EXAMPLES IN
C.S.E. MATHEMATICS
(METRIC EDITION)

R. L. BOLT, M.Sc.

Senior Mathematics Master,
Woodhouse Grove School

J. M. DENT & SONS LTD

BEDFORD STREET, LONDON, W.C.2

SBN: 460 09477 7

PREFACE

THIS book contains exercises for the use of pupils preparing for the C.S.E. examinations. The C.S.E. syllabuses and examination papers vary greatly in scope and content and it is right that they should do so. Nevertheless, there is a core of material common to most and it is on this that the book has been prepared. Syllabuses and past papers have been studied carefully so that the material provided shall be useful to as wide a range of schools as possible and in planning each exercise attention has been given to the importance of the particular topic and to the need for practice examples on it.

R. L. B.

Second Edition

Decimal currency and metric units are used throughout this book.

CONTENTS

DATA AND FORMULAE

1 millimetre (mm)	$= \frac{1}{1000}$ metre (m)
1 centimetre (cm)	$= \frac{1}{100}$ metre
1 kilometre (km)	$= 1\,000$ metres
1 kilogramme (kg)	$= 1\,000$ grammes
1 litre (l)	$= 1\,000$ cubic centimetres (cm³)
1 are (a)	$= 100$ square metres (m²)
1 hectare (ha)	$= 100$ ares
1 square kilometre (km²)	$= 100$ hectares
1 knot	$= 1$ nautical mile per hour

$$\text{Speed} = \frac{\text{Distance}}{\text{Time}}, \qquad \text{Time} = \frac{\text{Distance}}{\text{Speed}}$$

$$\text{Distance} = \text{Speed} \times \text{Time}$$

$$\text{Gain (or Loss) per cent} = \frac{\text{Gain (or Loss)}}{\text{Cost Price}} \times 100$$

Simple Interest: $I = \dfrac{PRT}{100}$

Circle. Circumference: πd or $2\pi r$
    Area: πr^2

Parallelogram. Area: base $\times$ height

Triangle. Area: $\frac{1}{2}$ base $\times$ height

Trapezium. Area: $\frac{1}{2}(a + b)h$

Prism. Volume: area of base $\times$ height

Pyramid. Volume: $\frac{1}{3} \times$ (area of base) $\times$ height

Cylinder. Curved surface area: $2\pi rh$
    Volume: $\pi r^2 h$

Cone.   Volume: $\frac{1}{3}\pi r^2 h$

Sphere.   Volume: $\frac{4}{3}\pi r^3$

$\pi \simeq 3\frac{1}{7}$ or $3{\cdot}1416$

Identities. $(a + b)(c + d) = ac + ad + bc + bd$
$$(a + b)^2 = a^2 + 2ab + b^2$$
$$(a - b)^2 = a^2 - 2ab + b^2$$
$$(a + b)(a - b) = a^2 - b^2$$

Indices. $a^x \times a^y = a^{x+y}$, $a^x \div a^y = a^{x-y}$, $(a^x)^y = a^{xy}$
$$a^o = 1, a^{\frac{1}{q}} = \sqrt[q]{a}, a^{-x} = \frac{1}{a^x}$$

Logarithms. $\log a + \log b = \log ab$
$$\log a - \log b = \log \frac{a}{b}$$
$$n \log a = \log a^n$$
$$\log_{10} 1 = 0, \log_{10} 10 = 1, \log_{10} 100 = 2$$

$\tan \theta = \dfrac{y}{x}$, $\sin \theta = \dfrac{y}{z}$, $\cos \theta = \dfrac{x}{z}$

Pythagoras' Theorem: $x^2 + y^2 = z^2$

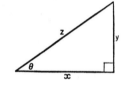

NUMBER: THE FOUR RULES

Exercise 1

Copy the following and fill in the missing figures:

1. Addition

```
 18*9
 50*
 2*76
  87
*836
```

2. Addition

```
 64*
  27
 1*9
*860
3*89
```

3. Subtraction

```
 5*82
 *63*
 4*5
```

4. $6* \times 7 = **2$

5. $3*7 \times 8 = 3*7*$

6. Multiplication

```
 *7*
  4*
1488
**32
*****
```

7. Division (No remainder)

```
      6*
3*)****
     *22
     29*
     ***
```

8. What must be added to 5,263 so that it can be divided exactly by 37?

9. Find the number N if $23 \times 35 \times N = 33,005$.

10. When working a division sum a boy divided by **34** instead of by **43**. His answer was **301**. What was the correct answer?

FACTORS, POWERS, MULTIPLES

Exercise 2

1. Which of the following numbers have 7 as a factor: 154; 275; 727; 2,674?

3

2. Which of the following numbers have 9 as a factor: 91; 567; 3,897; 9,592?

3. Which numbers between 30 and 70 have both 3 and 7 as factors?

4. Which numbers between 44 and 66 have both 4 and 6 as factors?

5. State the prime numbers between 100 and 120.

6. Which of the following are prime numbers: 41; 51; 53; 69; 73?

7. Write down the squares of 3, 7, 11 and 12.

8. Which of the following numbers are perfect squares and what are their square roots: 25; 44; 81; 169; 90; 400?

9. Write down the cubes of 2, 3 and 4.

10. Find the cubes of 6 and 55.

11. What are the values of 2^4; 2^7; $3^2 \times 5$; $7^2 \times 10^3$; $1^5 \times 10^2$?

12. Write down in index form $2 \times 2 \times 2 \times 3 \times 5 \times 5$; $7 \times 7 \times 7 \times 7$; $5 \times 7 \times 3 \times 7 \times 3$.

13. Write down all the factors of 36. Which are prime numbers? Which are perfect squares?

14. $90 = 2 \times 3^2 \times 5$. Express each of the following numbers in this way: 12; 75; 112; 100.

15. Express 324 as a product of prime numbers (as in Question 14) and hence find the square root of 324. Do the same for 676; 1,156; 3,025.

16. Express 28 and 21 as products of prime numbers and find the smallest number which is a multiple of both. Do the same for 18 and 24; 20 and 25; 32 and 40.

17. Write down the multiples of 8 which are less than 100 and the multiples of 12 which are less than 100. Which are common multiples of 8 and 12? Which is the lowest common multiple?

18. Repeat question 17 for the numbers 18 and 15 up to 200.

19. Express 36 and 40 as products of prime numbers. Hence find the lowest common multiple of 36 and 40.

20. Write down *all* the factors of 84. Write down all the factors of 112. Which numbers are factors of both 84 and 112? What is the highest common factor of 84 and 112?

21. Express 54 and 78 as products of prime numbers. Hence find the highest common factor of 54 and 78. Do the same for 35 and 60; 48 and 64; 308 and 242; 525 and 735.

22. Express 1,890 as the product of prime numbers. Use this result to find all numbers between 40 and 60 which will divide exactly into 1890.

23. Write down pairs of values of x and y such that $x + y = 50$ and both x and y are prime numbers.

24. a and b are any two prime numbers greater than 2. Why is $a + b$ always even? What can you say about $a - b$ and about $a \times b$?

25. Verify that $\qquad 1 + 3 + 5 + 7 + 9 = 5^2$
and that
$$1^3 + 2^3 + 3^3 + 4^3 + 5^3 = (1 + 2 + 3 + 4 + 5)^2$$
State similar results for
$$1 + 3 + 5 + 7 + 9 + 11 + 13$$
and $\qquad 1^3 + 2^3 + 3^3 + 4^3 + 5^3 + 6^3 + 7^3$
State the total of the first n odd numbers.

SCALES OF NOTATION

EXERCISE 3

1. What binary numbers correspond to the denary numbers 7, 10, 9, 19, 45, 106?

2. What denary numbers correspond to the binary numbers 101, 110, 1110, 10010, 11011, 101100?

Work out the following binary scale questions, leaving your answers in binary form:

3. $101 + 110$; $\quad 110 + 11$; $\quad 1010 + 110 + 1101$

4. $1101 - 10$; $\quad 10111 - 1010$; $\quad 11100 - 10111$

5. 1011×101; 11001×110; 1011×1101

6. $1001 \div 11$; $100011 \div 111$; $1001101 \div 1011$

Change the following numbers to the binary system, perform the process stated, and convert the answers to the denary system:

7. $26 + 38$ **8.** $45 - 28$

9. 23×14 **10.** $132 \div 11$

11. Express these bicimals as decimals: $0 \cdot 1$, $0 \cdot 01$, $0 \cdot 011$.

12. Express these binary fractions as denary fractions: $\frac{1}{10}$, $\frac{1}{11}$, $\frac{1}{110}$.

13.   (i) Add 5 and 6 in the scale of 8.
      (ii) Subtract 3 from 12 in the scale of 8.

14.   (i) Add 9 and 6 in the scale of 12.
      (ii) Subtract 7 from 14 in the scale of 12.

15.   (i) Add 3 and 5 in the scale of 6.
      (ii) Subtract 5 from 23 in the scale of 6.

16.   (i) Add 34 and 56 in the scale of 8.
      (ii) Subtract 65 from 242 in the scale of 8.

17. Write out the multiplication tables for 4 and 5 in the scale of 8. [Stop at $10_8 \times 4$ and $10_8 \times 5$.]

18. What scales are used in the following additions:
   (i) $156 + 167 = 334$ (ii) $345 + 543 = 1\ 221$?

19. What scales are used in the following statements:
   (i) $32 \times 12 = 414$ (ii) $242 \times 13 = 4\ 301$?

MONEY, WEIGHTS AND MEASURES

EXERCISE 4

1. How many 50 g bars of chocolate can be made from 35 kg?

2. The thickness of a five pence coin is $1 \cdot 8$ mm. What is the value of a pile of such coins of height 90 mm?

3. If the average length of my pace is 0·8 m, how many paces do I take in ½ km?

4. A train left London at 07.10 h and was due at Perth at 16.50 h. It arrived at 17.37 h. How long did it take and how late was it?

5. How many packets weighing 240 g can be made from 30 kg?

6. A pail weighs 8·2 kg when full of water and 4·8 kg when half full. What does it weigh when a quarter full?

7. 27 men hire a coach to take them to a football match. If the coach costs £22·95, how much should each man pay?

8. A collection box on a flag day contains the following coins: 68 of 1p, 42 of 2p, 85 of 5p and 15 of 10p. Find the total value of the coins.

9. Each week a man works from 8.30 a.m. to 12.45 p.m. on six days and from 1.30 p.m. to 5.30 p.m. on five days. His rate of pay is 48p per hour. Find his weekly wage.

10. A single lead shot weighs 2·15 g. Find, in kilogrammes, the weight of 10 000 lead shots. How many weigh 1 kg?

11. A clock loses 1 min 15 s each day. After how many days will it be 1 h slow?

12. In a certain district electricity costs 3·4p per unit for the first 60 units and then 0·5p per unit. Find the cost of 288 units.

13. Find the cost of fertilizer for a garden 24 m by 15 m if it is applied at 100 g per m² and costs 15p for a 4 kg bag.

14. High tide at Westsea on 1st August is at 11.32 a.m. If the time between consecutive high tides is 12 h 25 min, find the times of the two high tides on 15th August.

FRACTIONS

Give the value of:

1. $\frac{2}{3}$ hour   **2.** $\frac{5}{6}$ day   **3.** $\frac{3}{4}$ minute   **4.** $\frac{2}{5}$ minute

Complete:

5. $\frac{3}{4} = \frac{}{8} = \frac{}{12}$ **6.** $\frac{15}{25} = \frac{}{5} = \frac{}{10} = \frac{}{35}$

7. $\frac{11}{3} = 3\frac{}{3}$ **8.** $\frac{25}{6} = 4\frac{}{6}$ **9.** $2\frac{2}{5} = \frac{}{5}$ **10.** $5\frac{3}{7} = \frac{}{7}$

Express as fractions having the same denominator:

11. $\frac{2}{5}, \frac{3}{4}, \frac{7}{10}$ **12.** $\frac{4}{9}, \frac{1}{2}, \frac{2}{3}, \frac{5}{6}$

Place in order of size with the greatest first:

13. $\frac{5}{8}, \frac{3}{5}, \frac{13}{20}$ **14.** $\frac{4}{15}, \frac{5}{12}, \frac{2}{5}, \frac{1}{3}$

Draw figures to illustrate:

15. $\frac{2}{3} = \frac{4}{6}$ **16.** $\frac{1}{3} + \frac{1}{6} = \frac{1}{2}$

17. $\frac{2}{3} + \frac{1}{4} = \frac{11}{12}$ **18.** $\frac{2}{3}$ of $\frac{4}{5} = \frac{8}{15}$

Simplify:

19. $\frac{5}{12} + \frac{7}{18}$ **20.** $\frac{3}{4} + \frac{2}{3}$ **21.** $1\frac{3}{8} + 2\frac{1}{6}$

22. $\frac{5}{7} - \frac{1}{2}$ **23.** $3\frac{7}{10} - 1\frac{1}{4}$ **24.** $3\frac{3}{8} - \frac{7}{16}$

25. $\frac{2}{7} \times \frac{3}{5}$ **26.** $\frac{7}{9} \times \frac{3}{4}$ **27.** $1\frac{1}{3} \times 1\frac{2}{5}$

28. $2\frac{2}{3} \times 1\frac{1}{4}$ **29.** $6 \times 5\frac{1}{3}$ **30.** $2\frac{1}{4} \times 12$

31. $\frac{6}{7} \div 3$ **32.** $2\frac{2}{5} \div 6$ **33.** $\frac{1}{4} \div \frac{1}{3}$

34. $\frac{2}{3} \div \frac{2}{5}$ **35.** $1\frac{3}{4} \div 4\frac{1}{5}$ **36.** $5\frac{1}{7} \div 2\frac{4}{7}$

37. $2\frac{4}{5} \times \frac{2}{7} \times 1\frac{1}{4}$ **38.** $3\frac{1}{2} - 5\frac{2}{3} + 2\frac{1}{6}$

39. $\left(\frac{3}{4} - \frac{1}{3}\right) \times \frac{2}{5}$ **40.** $\left(2\frac{5}{12} - 1\frac{7}{15}\right) \times 1\frac{1}{4}$

41. $\left(1\frac{2}{3}\right)^2 \div 1\frac{1}{4}$ **42.** $\left(7\frac{5}{8} - 5\frac{3}{5}\right) \times 5\frac{1}{3}$

43. $2\frac{1}{3} \times \left(3\frac{1}{3} + 1\frac{1}{6}\right)$ **44.** $\frac{7}{16} \div \left(\frac{4}{5} - \frac{3}{4}\right)$

45. $\dfrac{1\frac{1}{3} - \frac{1}{6}}{1\frac{1}{3} + \frac{1}{6}}$ **46.** $\dfrac{8\frac{1}{3} \times 1\frac{1}{6}}{4\frac{1}{2} + 4\frac{1}{4}}$

47. A boy has $62\frac{1}{2}$p. He spends $\frac{3}{5}$ of this. How much has he left?

48. I start on a train journey of 120 km. The train stops at a station after 25 km. What fraction of the journey is still to be done?

49. During an influenza epidemic $\frac{3}{5}$ of a class are absent. If 14 pupils are present, how many are there in the class?

50. How many plots of land of area $\frac{5}{8}$ hectare can be obtained from an area of $13\frac{3}{4}$ hectares?

Express in pence:

51. $£\frac{3}{5}$ **52.** $£\frac{7}{20}$ **53.** $£\frac{11}{25}$ **54.** $£\frac{5}{8}$

Express in minutes and seconds:

55. $\frac{2}{9}$ hour   **56.** $\frac{9}{16}$ hour

Find in pence:

57. $\frac{3}{8}$ of £1·20   **58.** $\frac{4}{15}$ of £7·95

Find, correct to the nearest penny:

59. $\frac{2}{7}$ of £1   **60.** $\frac{2}{3}$ of 85p

61. Express 60p as a fraction of £4.

62. Express 45 minutes as a fraction of a day.

63. A long-playing gramophone record costs £1·65 which includes 45p purchase tax. Express the tax as a fraction of the total cost.

64. A flag-pole 6·3 m long is sunk 1·4 m into the ground. What fraction of the pole is above the ground?

DECIMALS

EXERCISE 6

Simplify:

1. 2·4 + 0·16	**2.** 4·07 + 6·5	**3.** 3·07 − 0·6
4. 5·2 − 0·04	**5.** 5 − 2·32	**6.** 3·72 × 10
7. 2·4 × 100	**8.** 0·06 × 10	**9.** 6·7 ÷ 100
10. 0·24 ÷ 10	**11.** 0·368 ÷ 4	**12.** 5·22 ÷ 3
13. 0·3 × 0·2	**14.** 0·7 × 0·8	**15.** 0·22 × 0·1

16. $(0.4)^2$ **17.** $(0.12)^2$ **18.** 4.6×30

19. $3 - (0.2)^2$ **20.** $\sqrt{0.09}$ **21.** $8 + 8.8 + 0.88$

22. $\dfrac{0.3 \times 0.143}{0.11}$ **23.** $\dfrac{0.7 \times 0.09}{3}$ **24.** $\dfrac{(0.2)^3 \times 30}{(0.4)^2}$

25. Give correct to 2 decimal places:

$$3.837; \quad 2.4487; \quad 26.572; \quad 0.0782$$

26. Give correct to 1 decimal place:

$$5.686; \quad 26.24; \quad 0.085; \quad 17.98$$

27. Give correct to 2 significant figures:

$$6.47; \quad 364.2; \quad 0.0736; \quad 0.2954$$

Express as decimals:

28. $\frac{2}{5}$ **29.** $\frac{9}{20}$ **30.** $\frac{7}{50}$ **31.** $\frac{2}{25}$

Express as fractions in their lowest terms:

32. 0.8 **33.** 0.06 **34.** 0.55 **35.** 0.375

Express as decimals correct to 3 decimal places:

36. $\frac{2}{3}$ **37.** $\frac{4}{7}$ **38.** $\frac{7}{12}$ **39.** $\frac{2}{33}$

Find the value of:

40. 2.4×1.9 **41.** 0.35×7.2 **42.** $(0.34)^2$

43. $8.51 \div 2.3$ **44.** $2.368 \div 6.4$ **45.** $1.464 \div 0.48$

46. If $4.928 \times 37.5 = 184.8$ what is the value of 49.28×0.375?

Express as recurring decimals:

47. $\frac{3}{11}$ **48.** $\frac{3}{7}$ **49.** $\frac{2}{9}$ **50.** $\frac{3}{13}$

Express as decimals of 1 yd., correct to 2 decimal places:

51. Express in metres: 62 cm; 54 mm; 328 cm; 7 mm.

52. Express in kilogrammes: 25 g; 4 729 g; 3 g; 150 g.

53. Express in metres: 5.8 km; 6.5 cm; 0.6 km; 30 mm.

54. Express 38 g as a decimal of 4 kg.

55. Express 400 g as a decimal of 7 kg, correct to 2 significant figures.

56. Express 3.7 km as a decimal of 9 km, correct to 2 decimal places.

57. Express as decimals of 1 hour: 24 minutes; 39 minutes.

58. Express in minutes: 0·7 hour; 0·85 hour.

59. Express $32\frac{1}{2}$p as an exact decimal of £1 and use the result to find the cost of 2 000 articles at $32\frac{1}{2}$p.

60. A motorist travelled 13 400 km in a year and spent £126 on petrol, oil and repairs. Find the cost per kilometre, correct to 0·01p.

PERCENTAGES

Exercise 7

1. Copy and complete:

Fraction	$\frac{1}{4}$	....	....	$\frac{5}{8}$	$\frac{1}{3}$	....
Decimal	....	0·4	....	....	....	0·03
Percentage	....	....	15	....	....	....

2. Express as fractions in their lowest terms:
85%, 36%, $37\frac{1}{2}\%$, $2\frac{1}{2}\%$, $23\frac{3}{4}\%$

3. Express as percentages:
$\frac{2}{5}$, $\frac{3}{20}$, $\frac{2}{3}$, $0·472$, $\frac{3}{7}$

4. (i) Find 24% of £75.
(ii) Express 42p as a percentage of 75p.
(iii) Find the sum of money of which £21 is 30%.

5. (i) Express £2·40 as a percentage of £3·75.
(ii) Find the value of 35% of £2.
(iii) Find the sum of money of which £42 is 75%.

6. An article costs £10. Find its price after an increase of (i) 20%, (ii) 25%, (iii) 7%.

7. Decrease a price of £12 by (i) 25%, (ii) $33\frac{1}{3}\%$, (iii) 50%.
Complete the following:

	Cost Price	*Selling Price*	*Profit*	*Profit* $\%$
8.	£24	£42		
9.	75 fr.			24%
10.		$81		35%
11.		£252		$12\frac{1}{2}\%$

12. Find as a percentage the difference between 0·3 and $\frac{1}{4}$.

13. A bill for £176 is reduced by a $12\frac{1}{2}\%$ discount. What sum should be paid?

14. After being reduced by 12%, the cost of an article was £5·50. Find the original cost.

15. A candidate in an examination gets 52 marks out of 80 on one paper and 102 marks out of 150 on another. Give each mark as a percentage and state the difference between them.

16. At a sale the prices are reduced by 35%. Find the sale price of an article originally costing £3·50.

17. In an examination a boy does not hand in a sheet of paper on which he could have scored 9 marks. As a result he gets 40% instead of 46%. How many marks did he receive?

18. A house agent's commission on the sale of a house is 5% of the first £300 and $2\frac{1}{2}\%$ of the remainder. Find his commission on a house sold for £3 750.

19. A man sells a car for £540 thereby losing 40% of what he paid for it. Find how much he paid for it.

20. 480 oranges are bought for £7·68 and sold at 2p each. Find the profit per cent on the cost price.

AVERAGES

EXERCISE 8

1. A batsman has the following scores: 16, 34, 2, 28, 19, 51, 18 and 0. Find his average.

2. On a cycling tour, a Youth Hosteller travels the following daily distances: 102 km, 82 km, 115 km, 48 km and 93 km. Find his daily average.

3. The average mark for a test in one class of 28 pupils was 48 and in another class of 32 pupils it was 68. Calculate the average mark for the group of 60 pupils.

4. In five tests a girl gets 48, 70, 32, 43 and 28 marks. How many must she get in the next test so that her average is 50?

5. The average weight of a boat crew of eight men is 69·2 kg. A man weighing 67·8 kg is replaced by one weighing 72·6 kg. Find the new average weight.

6. The average age of a class of 28 pupils is 16 yr 3 m. When eight pupils leave the average is reduced by 2 m. Calculate the average age of those who leave.

7. The barometer readings at 9.0 a.m. each day for a week were 1 012, 1 014, 1 000, 999, 1 005, 980, 971 millibars. Find the average reading, correct to 0·1 millibar.

8. (i) Write down the average of a, b and c.
    (ii) Write down the average weight of x parcels weighing p grammes each and y parcels weighing t grammes each.

9. What weight of a substance worth 15 fr per kg must be mixed with 24 kg worth 8 fr per kg to make a mixture worth 11 fr per kg?

10. In tests a boy gets 48 out of 60, 42 out of 90 and 36 out of 50. Find his average as a percentage of the total marks.

SPEEDS

EXERCISE 9

1. A car travels 21 km in $17\frac{1}{2}$ min. Find its speed in km/h.

2. How long does an aircraft travelling at 440 km/h take for a journey of 1 672 kilometres?

3. A car is travelling at 50 km/h. How far, correct to the nearest metre, does it travel in 1 minute?

4. Convert the speed of 35 metres per second to kilometres per hour.

5. Express 90 km/h and 54 km/h in metres per second.

6. A sprinter runs 100 metres in 13·2 seconds. Find his average speed in kilometres per hour, correct to the nearest unit.

7. A motorist travels 20 km in $\frac{1}{4}$ h, 68 km in 50 min, and 17 km in 25 min. Find his average speed for the whole journey.

8. A train is 150 metres long. How many seconds does it take to pass an observer if its speed is 108 km/h?

9. A man walking at 5 km/h takes 115 strides per minute. How many strides does he take in 100 metres?

10. Two cyclists start from towns 21 km apart and travel towards each other. One has a speed of 16 km/h and the other a speed of 19 km/h. How long is it before they meet and how far has each travelled?

11. A car travels 40 km at 40 km/h and 40 km at 60 km/h. Find its average speed.

12. A train travels for 3 hrs at 90 km/h and for 2 hrs at 60 km/h. Find its average speed.

13. A motor-boat can travel at 20 km/h in still water. How long does it take to travel (i) 8 km upstream, (ii) 8 km downstream if the speed of the current is 4 km/h? What is the average speed for the 16 km.

RATIO

EXERCISE 10

1. Divide £7 in the ratio 3:5:6.

2. The sides of a triangle are in the ratio 4:5:7 and the perimeter is 24 cm. Find the longest side.

3. A sum of money is divided in the ratio 3:5. The larger part is £465. Find the smaller part.

4. (i) Increase £1 in the ratio 5:4.
    (ii) Decrease £1 in the ratio 4:5.

5. Find the ratio of the areas of two squares having sides of 6 cm and 8 cm.

6. Bronze is made of copper, tin and zinc in the ratio 95:4:1 by weight. How many grammes of tin are needed for 2·5 kg of bronze?

7. Divide 82 francs among A, B and C so that A's share is $\frac{2}{5}$ of B's and B's is $\frac{3}{4}$ of C's.

8. Three partners share a profit in the following way: P gets $\frac{1}{3}$ of the profit and the remainder is shared between Q and R in the ratio 3:2. If R gets £30 how much does P get?

9. The scale on a map is 5 cm to 1 km. What distance in metres is represented by 2·4 cm and what area in hectares is represented by a rectangle 2·4 cm by 1·5 cm?

10. On a map 4 square centimetres represent 1 hectare. What length in centimetres represents 1 km?

11. On the plan of an abbey 2 mm represents 1 m. The cloister measures 172 mm by 28 mm. Find, in square metres, the area of the cloister.

PROPORTION

Exercise 11

1. A train travels 260 metres in 12 seconds. How far does it travel in $\frac{1}{2}$ minute?

2. Tom takes 64 paces when walking the length of a corridor and Jack takes 60 paces. Tom's pace is 75 cm. How long is Jack's pace?

3. A car can travel 92 km on 12 litres of petrol. How far will it go on 30 litres?

4. At 72 km/h a journey takes 12 min. How long would it take at 96 km/h?

5. A market gardener can grow 6 000 plants in $2\frac{1}{2}$ hectares. How many can he grow in $4\frac{3}{4}$ hectares?

6. A wheel of 18 teeth drives a second wheel having 30 teeth. If the speed of the first wheel is 45 revolutions per second, find the speed of the second wheel.

7. A hotel has sufficient food for 21 guests for 6 days. How long would it last 9 guests?

8. John receives 450 Austrian schillings for £6·25. How many should Paul receive for £11·12½?

9. If 9 looms weave 675 metres of cloth in 5 hours, how many metres will 4 looms weave in 6 hours?

10. A contractor estimates that it will take 30 men working 8 hours a day 35 days to complete a job. He has only 24 men available and must do the job in 42 days. How long must the men work each day?

11. The H.P. terms for a bicycle comprise a deposit of £3 and 12 monthly payments of £1·80. What should be the monthly payment if the deposit is raised to £6?

INTEREST

Exercise 12

Find the Simple Interest on:

1. £250 at 4% p.a. for 3 years.

2. £84 at 5% p.a. for 4 years.

3. 2,600 fr. at 3½% p.a. for 6 years.

4. $724 at 4½% p.a. for 5 years.

5. The interest on £720 after 6 years is £216. Find the rate.

6. The interest on £290 at 6% p.a. is £87. Find the time.

7. What sum of money invested for 4 years at 5½% p.a. gives an interest of 495 fr.?

8. In how many years will £100 amount to £200 at 5% p.a.?

9. What sum of money invested at 4% p.a. for 5 years will amount to £408?

10. What sum of money invested at 3% p.a. for 8 years will amount to 1,271 francs?

11. Find the Compound Interest on £500 at 4% p.a. for 2 years.

12. Find the Compound Interest on 350 fr. at 6% p.a. for 2 years.

13. How much more is obtained in 2 years by investing £750 at 5% Compound Interest instead of at 5% Simple Interest?

14. Each year the value of a car falls by 10% of its value at the beginning of the year. A certain car was worth £450 last January. What will it be worth (i) next January, (ii) the following January?

15. Each year the value of the machinery in a certain factory decreases by $12\frac{1}{2}$%. Calculate the value after 3 years of machinery costing originally £51,200.

16. A man borrowed £300 at 6% p.a. Compound Interest. He repaid £100 at the end of each year. How much did he still owe at the beginning of the third year?

USE OF TABLES

EXERCISE 13

Use tables to find approximate values for:

1. $43 \cdot 7^2$; 122^2; $0 \cdot 437^2$; $0 \cdot 122^2$

2. $\sqrt{3 \cdot 68}$; $\sqrt{368}$; $\sqrt{0 \cdot 0368}$; $\sqrt{0 \cdot 00368}$

3. $\dfrac{1}{4 \cdot 257}$; $\dfrac{1}{42 \cdot 57}$; $\dfrac{1}{0 \cdot 4257}$; $\dfrac{1}{0 \cdot 04257}$

4. $\dfrac{1}{4 \cdot 37} + \dfrac{1}{12 \cdot 68}$ **5.** $\dfrac{1}{0 \cdot 706} - \dfrac{1}{0 \cdot 853}$

6. $16 \cdot 72^2 + 10 \cdot 34^2$ **7.** $\sqrt{(4 \cdot 68^2 + 3 \cdot 79^2)}$

8. $\sqrt{(0 \cdot 673^2 + 0 \cdot 582^2)}$ **9.** $\sqrt{0 \cdot 872} - \sqrt{0 \cdot 0872}$

10. Write down the logarithms of $7 \cdot 148$, $714 \cdot 8$, $0 \cdot 07148$.

11. Write down the numbers for which the logarithms are $0 \cdot 3764$, $1 \cdot 3764$, $\bar{3} \cdot 3764$.

Simplify:

12. $\bar{3}{\cdot}5 + \bar{2}{\cdot}7$; $\bar{3}{\cdot}5 + 2{\cdot}7$; $4{\cdot}6 + \bar{1}{\cdot}9$; $\bar{4}{\cdot}6 + \bar{1}{\cdot}9$

13. $\bar{4}{\cdot}2 - \bar{1}{\cdot}8$; $4{\cdot}2 - \bar{1}{\cdot}8$; $\bar{4}{\cdot}2 - 1{\cdot}8$; $\bar{1}{\cdot}8 - \bar{4}{\cdot}2$

14. $2{\cdot}8 \times 3$; $\bar{2}{\cdot}8 \times 3$; $\bar{1}{\cdot}4 \times 5$; $\bar{3}{\cdot}9 \times 4$

15. $3{\cdot}6 \div 2$; $\bar{3}{\cdot}6 \div 2$; $\bar{3}{\cdot}6 \div 5$; $\bar{4}{\cdot}4 \div 3$

Use logarithms to evaluate:

16. $35{\cdot}24 \times 4{\cdot}35$

17. $263{\cdot}7 \div 38{\cdot}2$

18. $(12{\cdot}7)^3$

19. $\sqrt[3]{462}$

20. $\dfrac{462{\cdot}7}{32{\cdot}6}$

21. $\dfrac{260{\cdot}4 \times 23{\cdot}58}{62{\cdot}74}$

22. $\sqrt{\dfrac{19{\cdot}2}{3{\cdot}14}}$

23. $\dfrac{\sqrt{78{\cdot}3}}{2{\cdot}9}$

24. $72{\cdot}64 \times 0{\cdot}829$

25. $0{\cdot}937 \times 0{\cdot}879$

26. $32{\cdot}6 \div 468$

27. $0{\cdot}1723 \div 0{\cdot}0356$

28. $(0{\cdot}825)^3$

29. $\sqrt[3]{0{\cdot}825}$

30. $\dfrac{27{\cdot}34}{0{\cdot}367}$

31. $\dfrac{84{\cdot}15 \times 0{\cdot}4907}{0{\cdot}7246}$

32. $\sqrt{54{\cdot}03 \times 0{\cdot}6214}$

33. $\sqrt{0{\cdot}4293 \div 0{\cdot}8646}$

Use logarithms to evaluate to 3 significant figures:

34. $\dfrac{0{\cdot}734}{0{\cdot}294 \times 0{\cdot}063}$

35. $6{\cdot}284 \times \sqrt{\dfrac{423}{981}}$

36. $\dfrac{23{\cdot}47 \times \sqrt{98{\cdot}26}}{0{\cdot}806}$

37. $\dfrac{24{\cdot}7 \times (0{\cdot}624)^2}{\sqrt{7{\cdot}42}}$

38. 9^9 and $(0{\cdot}9)^9$

39. $(1{\cdot}5)^{20}$

40. How many digits are there in the expansion of 32^{10} and what are the two leading digits?

41. Express in the form $\log n$:

$\log 3 + \log 6$; $\log 12 - \log 2$; $3 \log 2$; $\frac{1}{2} \log 9$; $2 + \log_{10} 5$

42. If $\log 2 = 0{\cdot}30103$ find, without using tables, $\log 5$, $\log 8$ and $\log \frac{1}{2}$.

43. If $\log 7 = a$ and $\log 3 = b$, find, in terms of a and b:

$\log 21$; $\log \frac{7}{3}$; $\log 49$; $\log \sqrt{3}$; $\log 3^5$; $\log 700$; $\log 0.03$

44. If $\log p = x$ and $\log t = y$, express, in terms of x and y:

$\log pt$; $\log p^3$; $\log \dfrac{1}{t}$; $\log \sqrt{p}$

FOREIGN EXCHANGE

Exercise 14

1. If $£1 = 11.82$ French francs, how many francs are equivalent to $£35$?

2. If $£1 = 1\ 492$ Italian lire, how many lire are equivalent to $£6.50$?

3. How many German marks should I get for two $£10$ and one $£2$ Travellers' Cheques if $£1 = 9.46$ marks?

4. Find, correct to the nearest penny, the value of 1 U.S.A. dollar if $£1 = 2.38$ dollars.

5. A meal on a French train costs 13.20 francs. How much is this in British money, correct to the nearest penny, if 1 franc $\backsimeq 8\frac{1}{2}$p?

6. In a Swiss shop a watch is marked 42 francs. Convert this to sterling, correct to the nearest penny, given that $£1 = 10.27$ francs.

7. A tourist changes two $£10$ Travellers' Cheques into Austrian currency at 60.80 schillings to the $£$. He spends 893 schillings and changes the rest back into sterling at 62.20 schillings to the $£$. How much does he receive, correct to the nearest penny?

8. A Swiss hotel charges 22 francs per day, plus a service charge of 10%. Find the cost in sterling, correct to the nearest 10 pence, for a week at the hotel. $[£1 = 10.27$ francs$]$.

GRAPHS

EXERCISE 15

1. The figure shows the speed–time graph for a train.

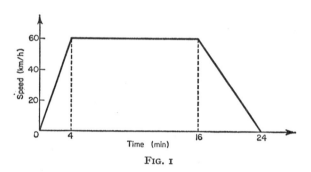

FIG. I

   (i) Describe the motion from 4 min to 16 min.

  (ii) What was the average speed for the first 4 min?

 (iii) How far did the train travel in the first 4 min?

 (iv) At what times was the speed 30 km/h?

  (v) Find the total distance travelled.

 (vi) Find the average speed, in km/h, for the whole journey.

2. Given that £1 = 17 Norwegian kroner, draw a graph for the conversion of British money up to £15 into Norwegian money. Take 1 cm to represent £1 and 20 kroner.

   (i) Use the graph to convert £11, £5·40, £12·80 and £74 into kroner.

  (ii) Use the graph to convert 100 kr, 160 kr, 226 kr and 800 kr into pounds and pence.

3. £100 is invested at 3% p.a. Compound Interest. The table shows its value, £A, after n years.

n	0	10	20	30	40	50
A	100	134	181	243	326	438

Plot these values taking 2 cm to represent 10 yr and £100. Join the points by a smooth curve which will represent the continuous growth of the sum of money.

(i) After how long is the value approximately £300?

(ii) What is the value after 25 yr?

4. On each stroke of an air pump the pressure in a vessel is reduced. The following table gives the pressure, p mm of mercury, after n strokes:

n	0	5	10	15	20	25	30
p	760	449	265	156	92	55	32

Plot these values taking 20 mm to 5 strokes and to 100 mm of mercury.

(i) What is the pressure after 18 strokes?

(ii) After how many strokes is the pressure just under a quarter of its original value?

5. The table shows the weight, w grammes, of a crystal growing in a 'mother' liquid after n days.

n	0	1	2	3	4	5
w	100	140	196	274	384	538

Draw a graph using 2 cm to 1 day and to 100 g.
When has the crystal (i) doubled its weight, (ii) quadrupled its weight?

6. In Wyeshire there are two systems of paying for electricity. On system A there is a charge of 2·5p for each unit used: on system B there is a basic charge of £3·20 and a charge of 0·5p for each unit used.

Draw graphs to show the cost up to 240 units, using 2 cm to 40 units and to £1.

(i) Find the cost of 100 units on each system.

(ii) Find the number of units for which the charge is the same on both systems.

7. A hiker left village A at 10.10 a.m. to walk to village C. 22 km from A. He passed through village B, which is 7 km from A, at 11.20 a.m. and later got a lift from a lorry which took him to C at an average speed of 24 km/h. He reached C at 12.20 p.m.

Draw a graph to show his distance from A at any time. Take 1 cm to 2 km and to 10 min.

Find from the graph the time at which he was picked up by the lorry and his walking speed.

Find also the latest time at which he could have got a lift by a car travelling at 48 km/h in order to reach C by 12.20 p.m.

MENSURATION: RECTANGULAR

EXERCISE 16

1. A rectangular field is 240 m long and 150 m wide. Calculate its area in hectares.

2. Find the weight of a rectangular metal plate 75 mm by 62 mm if 1 cm² weighs 4g.

3. How many square linoleum tiles of side 20 cm are needed to cover a floor 3·8 m by 2·8 m?

4. A rectangular tank is 38 cm long, 25 cm wide and 20 cm high. How many litres of water can it hold?

5. A piece of wire 14 cm long is to be bent to form a rectangle. In how many ways can this be done so that each side is a whole number of centimetres? State the different areas obtained. Is it possible to obtain a larger area by *not* restricting the lengths of the sides to whole numbers of centimetres? Will a circle give a larger area?

6. The total surface area of a cube is 54 cm². Find its volume.

7. A rectangular tank is 2 m long, 1·6 m wide and 1·5 m high.

Calculate its capacity in cubic metres. What is the depth of water in it when it contains 2 400 litres?

8. A cubical storage box has sides of 40 cm. Find the side of a cubical box which would hold twice as much.

9. Find the area of the triangle in Fig. 2.

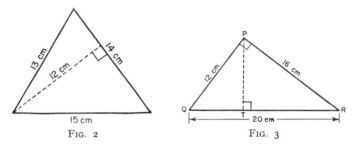

FIG. 2   FIG. 3

10. Find the area of the triangle in Fig. 3 and calculate PT.

11. Find the area of the trapezium in Fig. 4.

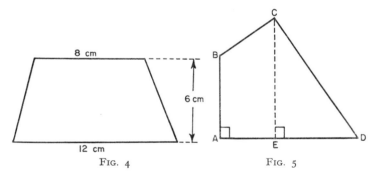

FIG. 4   FIG. 5

12. In Fig. 5, AB = 32 m, CE = 48 m, AE = 25 m and ED = 40 m. Calculate the area of the quadrilateral.

13. The area of $\triangle$PQR is 150 cm² and its perimeter is 60 cm. If PQ = 15 cm and the length of the perpendicular from P to side QR is 12 cm, calculate PR.

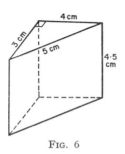

FIG. 6

14. [Fig. 6.] Draw a net for the solid, showing the folds by dotted lines. Calculate the volume and the surface area of the solid.

15. A pyramid stands on a square base of side 6 cm and has a height of 8 cm. Find its volume.

16. A pyramid has a square base of side 4 cm and four sloping edges of length 6 cm. Draw its net showing folds by dotted lines. After measuring a certain length, calculate the approximate area of the surface of the pyramid.

17. A swimming bath is 50 m long and 30 m wide and its walls are vertical. It is 1m deep at one end and 3 m deep at the other; the bottom slopes uniformly. Calculate the number of cubic metres of water in the bath.

It was filled by water flowing at 2 metres per second from a pipe of cross-section area 0·01 m². How long did it take?

18. Fig. 7 represents a garden shed. Calculate:

   (i) its capacity in cubic metres,
   (ii) the total area of its four walls,
   (iii) the area of the sloping roof. [Pythagoras' Theorem is needed.]

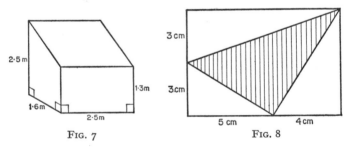

FIG. 7   FIG. 8

19. Fig. 8 shows a rectangle. Calculate the area of the shaded triangle.

20. Fig. 9 shows a solid pyramid. PQR is horizontal and PT is vertical. PQ = PR = 6 cm, PT = 8 cm. Calculate the volume.

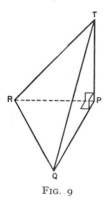

FIG. 9

Draw a net for the solid and after making some measurements find the total surface area.

MENSURATION: CIRCULAR

EXERCISE 17

[Take π as $3\frac{1}{7}$]

1. A car tyre has a radius of 28 cm. Find (i) its circumference, (ii) the number of revolutions it makes in 4·4 kilometres.

2. Some thin wire is wound on to a cylindrical drum of radius 35 mm. Find the length of 1 turn and of 150 turns.

3. A running track has two semi-circular ends of radius 63 metres and two straight lengths. The perimeter of the track is 1 000 metres. Find the length of each straight.

4. Find the area of a circle of radius 10·5 cm.

5. A circular fishpond of radius 2·4 m is surrounded by a path of width 0·7 m. Find the area of the path.

6. Two circles of diameter 7 cm are cut from a rectangular metal plate 16 cm by 8 cm. Find the area of the part left over.

7. [Fig. 10.] Calculate the shaded area.

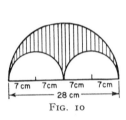

FIG. 10

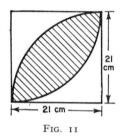

FIG. 11

8. [Fig. 11.] Calculate the shaded area.

9. Find the area of a paper label which just covers the curved surface of a cylindrical tin of diameter 8 cm and height $10\frac{1}{2}$ cm.

10. Find the capacity in litres of a cylindrical tank of diameter 35 cm and height 48 cm.

11. How many cylindrical cups each of height 7 cm and diameter 8 cm can be filled from a cask containing 20 litres?

12. Find, correct to the nearest unit, the curved surface area and the volume of a cylinder of height 8·4 cm and diameter 6·5 cm.

13. Calculate the volume of a cone of radius 7 cm and height 10 cm.

14. Calculate the volume and surface area of a sphere of radius $3\frac{1}{2}$ cm.

15. A cone of height 8 cm and radius 6 cm is carved from a rectangular block of wood 12 cm by 12 cm by 8 cm. Find:

   (i) the proportion of wood wasted:

   (ii) the weight of the cone if 1 cm³ of wood weighs 0·7 g.

16. A wooden post for fencing consists of a circular cylinder of diameter 8 cm and length 1·2 m with a cone of length 15 cm and diameter 8 cm at one end. Calculate the volume of the post in cubic centimetres, correct to the nearest unit.

17. A storage tank consists of a cylinder with a hemisphere at each end. The total length is 9 m and the radius is 2 m. Calculate the capacity, correct to the nearest cubic metre.

18. 693 m³ of water flow into a cylindrical tank of diameter 14 m. Find the rise in the water level.

19. A measuring cylinder of radius 3 cm contains water of depth 25 cm. Find the depth of the water if it is poured into another cylinder of radius 5 cm.

20. A cylinder of height 20 cm and radius 8 cm contains water to a height of 14 cm. A sphere of radius 6 cm is lowered into the water. Find the new height of the water.

21. (i) If Fig. 12 represents a triangle and a rectangle, express
    (*a*) the area of the triangle as a fraction of the area of the rectangle,
    (*b*) the area of X as a fraction of the area of Y.

  (ii) If Fig. 12 represents a cone in a cylinder, express
    (*a*) the volume of the cone as a fraction of the volume of the cylinder,
    (*b*) the volume of X as a fraction of the volume of Y.

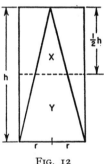

Fig. 12

MISCELLANEOUS PROBLEMS

EXERCISE 18

1. A householder used 422 units of electricity for heating and 318 for lighting. He paid 0·4p per unit for heating and 1·9p per unit for lighting. He could have paid a flat rate of 0·5p per unit together with a fixed charge of £2. How much would he have saved?

2. A man is paid a salary of £840 for his first year and receives an increase of £40 at the end of each year. Calculate his salary for the sixth year.

Each year he pays 6% of his salary to a pension fund. At the end of six years he changes his job and the pension contributions are returned to him. How much does he receive?

3. A photographic dealer advertises his H.P. terms as a deposit of $7\frac{1}{2}$% of the cash price and 5% interest on the balance (the sum left when the deposit is deducted from the cash price). Find (i) the deposit and (ii) the 12 monthly payments for a camera of cash price £64. (Answer to the nearest penny.)

4. The H.P. terms for a washing machine costing £21 are as follows: A: £2 deposit and 12 quarterly payments of £1·80; B: £2·50 deposit and 8 monthly payments of £2·40. How much is saved by adopting B instead of A?

5. Purchase Tax on television sets was reduced from 60% of the wholesale price to 50% of it. How much was saved on a set for which the wholesale price was £40? If the retailer's profit on the set was $33\frac{1}{3}$% of the wholesale price what was the new retail price?

6. A man buys a house for £3 200 and borrows £2 600 from a Building Society. He is to repay the loan and interest on it at the rate of £230 per year for 20 years. How much will the house have cost him?

After 6 years he sells the house for £3 950. He has to pay £2 060 to settle his Building Society loan and £130 in solicitor's fees. How much cash will he have left? How much has it cost him to live in the house for the 6 years?

7. The rateable value of a city is £2 760 000 and a sum of £2 932 500 is required. What rate must be charged? What will a 1p rate produce? What must be paid by the owner of a shop assessed at £520?

8. A rate of 92p in the £ produces £578 680 in a certain district. What does a 1p rate produce? Find the rateable value of the district. How much is paid on a garage assessed at £92?

9. Income Tax is calculated on the income which remains after deduction of certain allowances. The chief allowances for 1969–70 were: Earned Income Allowance—$\frac{2}{9}$ of the total earned income for the year; Personal Allowance—£375 for a married man, £255 for a single man; Children's Allowance— £115 for each child not over 11 years, £140 for each child over 11 years but not over 16 years.

The first £260 of taxable income was taxed at the rate of 30% and the rest at 41·25 %.

    (i) Find the tax for a married man earning £1 350 if he had three children of ages 10, 12 and 15 years.

   (ii) Find the tax per week, correct to the nearest penny, for a single man earning £16 per week.

  (iii) How much, correct to the nearest pound, can a single man earn per year before he pays any tax at the top rate?

SUBSTITUTION

Exercise 19

If $a = 3$, $b = -1$, $c = \frac{1}{2}$, $d = 0$, $e = -2$, find the value of:

1. $a + e$; e^2; $\dfrac{1}{c}$; $a - e$; e^3; bd; be

2. $b + e + a$; $ce + d$; $cde + a$; $7b^2$

3. $2a - b - e$; c^2e^2; $(a + b - c)^2$; $(a + b)(d + e)$

4. $\dfrac{6c}{e}$; $\dfrac{a^2}{b}$; $\left(\dfrac{a}{b}\right)^2$; $\dfrac{a - b}{c}$

5. $2(a + b) + (ad - e)^2$; $\left(\dfrac{a - e}{b} - 3bc\right) \div \dfrac{b}{e}$

If $u = 4$, $w = 0$, $x = -3$, $y = 6$, $z = -\frac{1}{3}$, find the value of:

6. $3u + 2x - y$; $(u + x)(w - x)$; yz

7. x^2z; $uw - xy$; $(2u - y)(x - z)$

8. $\dfrac{ux}{y} + \dfrac{wz}{u}$; $\dfrac{u}{y} - z$; $\dfrac{y^2}{u} - \dfrac{x}{z}$

9. If $a = -1$ and $b = 2$ which has the greater value and by how much: (i) $(a - b)^2 + (a + b)^2$, (ii) $(a^2 - b^2) + (a^2 + b^2)$?

10. Find the value of $-b + \sqrt{b^2 - 4ac}$ when $a = 3$, $b = -2$, $c = -1$.

Find the value of:

11. $a^2 - 6a + 7$ (i) when $a = -2$, (ii) when $a = \frac{1}{2}$.

12. $a^2 - b^2 - 2a + 2b$ when $a = -3$ and $b = 2$.

13. $x^3 + y^3 + z^3$ when $x = 2$, $y = -1$ and $z = -3$.

14. $(x + y)^2 + (x - y)^2$ when $x = 2$ and $y = -3$.

15. By how much does $(a - b)^2$ exceed $a^2 - b^2$ when $a = 3$ and $b = -2$?

16. By how much does $(x - 2y)^2$ exceed $x^2 - 2y^2$ when $x = 2$ and $y = -2$?

17. Find the value of $\dfrac{x}{3} - \dfrac{x - 1}{2}$ (i) when $x = -3$, (ii) when $x = -\frac{1}{3}$.

18. Find the value of $2x^3 - 3x^2 - 4x + 5$ (i) when $x = -1$, (ii) when $x = -2$.

SIMPLIFICATION

EXERCISE 20

Simplify:

1. $4a + 9a + 3a$

2. $4b - 9b + 2b$

3. $3c + 5c + 7c$

4. $7d + 8d - d$

5. $4e + 2f - e + 3f$

6. $7g + 9h - 2h - 5g$

7. $6k - 2m + 2k - 5m$

8. $n - p + 7p - 2n$

9. $a \times a \times a$

10. $b \times b \times b \times b \times b$

11. $3a \times 2a$

12. $4b \times 2b$

13. $(5c)^2$

14. $3a \times 2b$

15. $a^2 \times a^3$

16. $b^3 \times b$

17. $2a^2 \times 3a^3$

18. $4a^2 \times 5b$

19. $(a^2)^3$

20. $(b^3)^5$

21. $(3c^3)^2$

22. $(\frac{1}{2}d^2)^3$

23. $a^7 \div a^2$

24. $b^6 \div b$

25. $14c \div 2c$

26. $18d \div 27d$

27. $20a^3 \div 5a$

28. $10a^4b^3 \div 2a^3b$

29. $3(a - 2b + c)$

30. $d(d - 2e + f)$

31. $-g(g - 5)$

32. $3h(2j - 5h)$

33. $k^2(k + 3)$

34. $-2m^2(7 - 4m)$

35. $\frac{1}{2}(6p - 5)$

36. $\frac{1}{5}(10 - t^2)$

37. $\frac{2}{3}(15 - 9v)$

38. $\frac{3}{4}(12x + 16y)$

39. $\sqrt{a^6}$

40. $\sqrt[3]{a^6}$

41. $\sqrt{(25a^8)} \times 2b$

42. $(4c^4)^2 \div 8c^3$

Exercise 21

Simplify:

1. $(a + b)(c + d)$

2. $(p - q)(p - r)$

3. $(c - 3)(d + 4)$

4. $(6 + f)(2 - g)$

5. $(x + 2)(x + 3)$

6. $(y + 4)(y + 6)$

7. $(a - 5)(a - 1)$

8. $(b - 6)(b - 3)$

9. $(c + 8)(c - 3)$

10. $(d + 2)(d - 7)$

11. $(2x + 3)(x + 5)$

12. $(y - 2)(3y - 5)$

13. $(3x - 1)(5x + 2)$

14. $(4 + 3y)(2 - y)$

15. $(3a - 2)(2a + 3)$

16. $(5b + 4)(2b - 3)$

17. $(x^2 + 6)(2x^2 + 3)$

18. $(7 - c)(4 + 3c)$

19. $(x + 4)^2$

20. $(y - 3)^2$

21. $(3a - 1)^2$

22. $(5b + 1)^2$

23. $(x + y)^2 + (x - y)^2$

24. $(a^2 - b^2) + (a - b)^2$

25. $(2a + 3)^2$

26. $(3b - 5)^2$

27. $(x + 7)(x - 7)$

28. $(y - 5)(y + 5)$

29. $(4x + 3y)^2$

30. $(3 + p)(3 - p)$

31. $(a + b)(a - b) + b^2$

32. $(p + q)^2 - 2pq$

33. $(x - y)^2 - (x^2 + y^2)$

34. $(2x + 3y)^2 - (2x - 3y)^2$

35. Draw a figure to illustrate the identity $(x + 5)(x + 3) \equiv x^2 + 8x + 15$

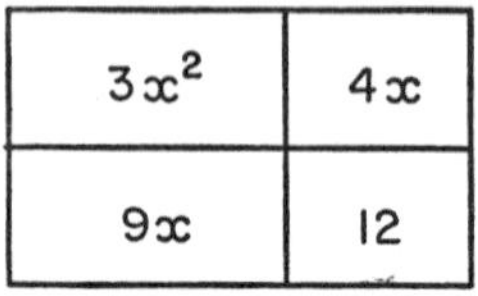

Fig. 13

36. Draw a figure to illustrate the expansion of $(a + b)^2$.

37. In Fig. 13, the areas of the small rectangles are shown in square centimetres. Find, in centimetres, the lengths of the sides of the large rectangle.

FACTORS

EXERCISE 22

Factorize:

1. $x^2 + 5x$

2. $ab - a$

3. $3c^2 - 6c$

4. $15d^2 + 20d^3$

5. $6x^2y^3 - 9x^3y^2$

6. $\pi r^2 + 2\pi rh$

7. $9abc - 6bcd$

8. $5x^3y^4 - 10x^4y^3 + 15x^5y^2$

9. $8m^4p^2 - 12m^2pq^3$

10. $18k^3n^2 - 27k^2n^3 - 9kn^4$

Factorize:

11. $a^2 - 9$

12. $25 - b^2$

13. $4c^2 - 1$

14. $9d^2 - 16$

15. $p^2q^2 - 1$

16. $36x^2 - 49$

17. $a^3 - 9a$

18. $b^3 - b$

19. $3c^2 - 75$

20. Factorize $a^2 - ab$. Use the result to find the value of $948^2 - 948 \times 938$.

21. Factorize $x^2 - y^2$. Use the result to find the value of $301^2 - 299^2$.

Questions 22 to 25. By factorizing, find the value of:

22. $253 \times 187 - 184 \times 253$

23. $55^2 - 45^2$

24. $(13\frac{1}{2})^2 - (6\frac{1}{2})^2$ **25.** $(65\cdot3)^2 - (34\cdot7)^2$

26. $\pi x^2 - \pi y^2$ when $\pi = 3\frac{1}{7}$, $x = 13$, $y = 8$

Factorize:

27. $a^2 + 5a + 6$ **28.** $b^2 + 7b + 10$ **29.** $c^2 - 6c + 5$

30. $d^2 - 6d + 8$ **31.** $a^2 + 5a - 6$ **32.** $b^2 + 3b - 10$

33. $c^2 - 4c - 5$ **34.** $d^2 - 2d - 8$ **35.** $e^2 + e - 12$

36. $1 + 7a + 6a^2$ **37.** $1 - b - 2b^2$ **38.** $10 - 11c + c^2$

39. $ab^2 - 4ab + 3a$ **40.** $2c^2 + 8c + 6$ **41.** $3d^2 - 3d - 18$

42. $2a^2 + 5a + 3$ **43.** $3b^2 - 5b + 2$ **44.** $3c^2 - 5c - 2$

45. $5d^2 + 2d - 3$ **46.** $2e^2 - e - 10$ **47.** $12f^2 + 14f - 6$

48. Factorize $a^2 - 2a - 3$, $b^2 + 2b - 3$ and $c^2 - 4c + 3$.

49. Write down the factors of $x^2 + 10x + 21$. Put $x = 10$ in the given expression and in your answer. What factors does this give for 221?

50. Factorize $4x^2 + 8x + 3$ and by putting $x = 10$ find the prime factors of 483.

Factorize:

51. $x(b + c) - y(b + c)$ **52.** $3p(2u - 5) + 2(2u - 5)$

53. $ab - bc + ad - cd$ **54.** $fh + 5h + 2f + 10$

55. $m^2 + mp - 3m - 3p$ **56.** $xy - 4x - y^2 + 4y$

57. $ab - 5a + 3b - 15$ **58.** $3c - d - 6cd + 2d^2$

59. $3ap + 6 - 9a - 2p$ **60.** $x^2 + 7y + 7x + xy$

61. $x + y + ax + ay$ **62.** $3p^2 - p - 6qp + 2q$

63. $1 - 2x - 4y^2 + 8xy^2$ **64.** $a + b + a^2 - b^2$

65. $12p - 3p^2 + 4pq - p^2q$ **66.** $2fg - 10f + 4g - 20$

Factorize:

67. $a^2 + 10a + 25$ **68.** $b^2 - 14b + 49$ **69.** $c^2 + 12c + 36$

70. $d^2 + \frac{2}{3}d + \frac{1}{9}$ **71.** $e^2 - e + \frac{1}{4}$ **72.** $1 + 6f + 9f^2$

73. $4x^2 + 4x + 1$ **74.** $9y^2 - 6y + 1$ **75.** $4z^2 - 12z + 9$

76. $ab^2 + 8ab + 16a$ **77.** $12p^2 - 12p + 3$ **78.** $x^4 - 16x^2 + 64$

Find the value of a, b and c so that the given expressions are perfect squares:

79. $x^2 - 18x + a$ **80.** $y^2 + 22y + b$ **81.** $z^2 - 2z + c$

Complete the following:

82. $x^2 + 20x + \ldots = (\ldots)^2$ **83.** $x^2 + \frac{2}{5}x + \ldots = (\ldots)^2$

84. $x^2 - \frac{1}{2}x + \ldots = (\ldots)^2$ **85.** $4x^2 - 12x + \ldots = (\ldots)^2$

FRACTIONS

EXERCISE 23

Simplify:

1. $\dfrac{ab}{ac}$; $\dfrac{10d^2}{5d}$; $\dfrac{4e^6}{6e^4}$; $\dfrac{-12fg}{4gh}$

2. $\dfrac{p^3r}{p}$; $\dfrac{-3t^5}{-6t}$; $\dfrac{8xy^2}{-2xy}$; $\dfrac{-2abc}{-10b^3}$

Complete:

3. $\dfrac{a}{b} = \dfrac{}{b^2} = \dfrac{a^2}{} = \dfrac{3a}{} = \dfrac{-2a}{}$

4. $\dfrac{3}{cd} = \dfrac{3d}{} = \dfrac{9}{} = \dfrac{}{cde} = \dfrac{3(c+d)}{}$

5. $\dfrac{a+b}{c} = \dfrac{a^2-b^2}{} = \dfrac{a^2+ab}{} = \dfrac{}{c^2}$

Simplify, giving each as a single fraction:

6. $\dfrac{a}{4} - \dfrac{a}{6}$ **7.** $\dfrac{1}{2b} + \dfrac{1}{3b}$ **8.** $\dfrac{3}{c} + \dfrac{2}{d}$

9. $\dfrac{7}{6g} - \dfrac{2}{3g}$ **10.** $\dfrac{h+3}{6} - \dfrac{h-2}{2}$ **11.** $\dfrac{m-1}{m} - \dfrac{p-1}{p}$

12. $\dfrac{t}{q} + \dfrac{q}{t}$ **13.** $\dfrac{1}{3xy} - \dfrac{5}{6yz} - \dfrac{1}{2zx}$

14. $\dfrac{3}{a^2} + \dfrac{2}{ab} - \dfrac{1}{b^2}$ **15.** $\dfrac{c+d}{c(c-d)} - \dfrac{1}{c-d}$

Simplify:

16. $\dfrac{3a - 3b}{6}$ **17.** $\dfrac{3a - 3b}{a - b}$ **18.** $\dfrac{c^2 - d^2}{c^2 + cd}$

19. $\dfrac{fg - g^2}{f^2 - g^2}$ **20.** $\dfrac{5h - 15}{h^2 - 2h - 3}$ **21.** $\dfrac{k^2 + 4k + 3}{k^2 + 3k}$

22. $\dfrac{a + 1}{6} - \dfrac{a - 3}{2}$ **23.** $\dfrac{c - 4}{15} + \dfrac{c + 6}{10}$

24. $\dfrac{5a^2}{2b} \div \dfrac{15a}{b^2}$ **25.** $\dfrac{d(f + d)}{3} \times \dfrac{6}{(f + d)}$

26. $\dfrac{(a + 2)(a + 3)}{a^2 - 4}$ **27.** $\dfrac{b(b - c)(3b - c)}{3b^2 - bc}$

28. If $a = x^2 + xy - 2y^2$, $b = x^2 - 2xy$ and $c = x^2 - 4y^2$, find the simplest answer in terms of x and y for

(i) $\dfrac{b}{c}$,   (ii) $\dfrac{c}{a}$,   (iii) $\dfrac{ab}{c}$.

SIMPLE EQUATIONS

Exercise 24

Solve:

1. $x + 2 = 9$ **2.** $x - 2 = 9$ **3.** $2x = 9$

4. $\frac{1}{2}x = 9$ **5.** $2x + 3 = 11$ **6.** $3x - 5 = 13$

7. $5x + 6 = 1$ **8.** $x + 20 = 2 - 5x$ **9.** $4x = 11$

10. $\frac{1}{4}x + 3 = 0$ **11.** $\frac{2}{3}x + 5 = 13$ **12.** $\frac{3}{4}x - 1 = 7$

13. $3(x - 2) = 15$ **14.** $\frac{1}{3}(x - 2) = 2$ **15.** $\frac{1}{4}(x + 3) = 5$

16. $2(x - 4) = 3(x - 2) - 7$ **17.** $5(x + 5) = 3(7 + x)$

18. $(x + 4)(x - 2) = x^2$ **19.** $2x(x + 3) - x(2x - 1) = 14$

20. $(x - 2)(x - 3) = (x + 4)(x + 1)$

21. $(x - 2)^2 = (x - 5)(x - 7) + 5$

22. $0 \cdot 8x - 2 \cdot 1 = 0 \cdot 5x$

23. $0 \cdot 2(3x + 1) = 1 \cdot 1x + 0 \cdot 8$

24. Find the missing figure in the equation $5x - 7 = 2x + ...$ so that the solution is $x = 4$.

25. Find the missing figure in the equation $(x + 1)(x - 4) = (x + 5)(x + ...)$ so that the solution is $x = -2$.

26. State the positive whole number values of x and y which satisfy $x + y = 5$.

27. Find the positive whole number values of a and b such that $2a + 3b = 23$.

Solve:

28. $\dfrac{x}{3} + \dfrac{x}{5} = 4$

29. $\dfrac{x}{2} - \dfrac{x + 3}{4} = 1$

30. $\dfrac{3x - 4}{2} - \dfrac{2x - 1}{3} = 2\frac{1}{2}$

31. $\dfrac{3x - 1}{5} + \dfrac{4x + 1}{3} = 4$

32. $\dfrac{x + 4}{6} - \dfrac{2x + 5}{3} = \frac{1}{2}$

33. $\dfrac{2x + 1}{8} + \dfrac{3 - x}{2} = 1\frac{3}{4}$

34. $\dfrac{1}{3x} + \dfrac{1}{4x} = \frac{7}{2}$

35. $\dfrac{1}{x} - \dfrac{1}{3x} = \frac{1}{6}$

36. The smallest of three consecutive whole numbers is x. Write down expressions for the other two. When three times the smallest is added to four times the middle number, the answer is six times the largest. Write down an equation for x and so find the three numbers.

37. A collection box contains the following: x coins of 10p each, $3x$ of 5p and $(4x + 1)$ of 2p. The total value of the coins is £2. Form an equation for x and solve it. How many 2p coins are there in the box?

38. A rectangle has sides of length $(x + 3)$ cm and $(x + 2)$ cm. Its area is 46 cm² greater than the area of a square of side x cm. Find x.

39. A cyclist makes a journey of 17 km. He does the first x km at an average speed of 20 km/h and the rest at an average speed of 12 km/h. State, in minutes, the times for each part of the journey. If the whole journey takes 1 h 9 min, write down an equation for x and solve it.

40. Two cars start at the same time on a journey of x km: car A travels at 80 km/h and car B travels at 60 km/h: A arrives $\frac{1}{2}$ h before B. Form an equation for x and solve it.

41. The angles of a triangle are $4x$, $2x + 10$ and $3x - 10$ degrees. Write down an equation for x and solve it. What kind of triangle is this?

42. A hiker has 26 min in which to catch the last bus home from a village 3 km away. He can walk at 6 km/h and run at 12 km/h. How far must he run in order to catch the bus?

SIMULTANEOUS LINEAR EQUATIONS

EXERCISE 25

Solve the following equations for x and y:

1. $x + y = 3$
   $3x - y = 5$

2. $x + 2y = 5$
   $2x + y = 1$

3. $x + y = 3$
   $x - 2y = 9$

4. $x + y = 7$
   $x + 3 = y$

5. $3x - 2y = 1$
   $x + 2y = 11$

6. $5x - 2y = 19$
   $2x + y = 4$

7. $4x + 3y = 2$
   $x + 4y = 7$

8. $3x - y = 3$
   $5x + 3y = -2$

9. $8x + 9y = 0$
   $12x + 6y = 5$

10. $5x + 2y = 3$
   $4x + 2 = 5y$

11. $8x - 7y = 13$
   $3x + 2y = 28$

12. $5x + 2y = 5$
   $4x + 3y + 3 = 0$

13. If $x + 3y = 5$ and $2x + 5y = 8$, find the value of $3x + 4y$.

14. If $4x + 3y = 6$ and $3x - 2y = 13$, find the value of $x + y$.

15. Solve $4x - 7y = 3x - 5y + 1 = 2$.

16. Solve $13x + y = x - 3y = 5$.

17. In a snack bar one party pays 26p for 5 coffees and 2 teas and another party pays 17p for 2 coffees and 3 teas. Find the price of a cup of coffee.

18. A café serves x lunches at 25p each and y lunches at 30p each. State (i) the total number of lunches served and (ii) the total money received. If these totals are 49 and £13, find x and y.

19. I wrote down two numbers which I will call x and y. I added 21 to x and the answer was twice y. I added 9 to y and the answer was twice x. Write down two equations and use them to find x and y.

20. An ice-cream seller charges Alice 25p for 5 wafers and 4 cornets and charges Betty 24p for 3 wafers and 6 cornets. How much should he charge Carol for 1 wafer and 2 cornets?

21. A rectangle has a length of x cm, a width of y cm, and a perimeter of 25 cm. If the width is doubled and the length is halved, the perimeter is 29 cm. Find x and y.

QUADRATIC EQUATIONS

EXERCISE 26

1. Find the value of $(x - 2)(x - 3)$ if $x = 5, 4, 3, 2, 0, -2$.

2. Find the value of $(x + 2)(x - 1)$ if $x = 3, 2, 1, 0, -1, -2$.

3. Find the value of $(3x - 1)(2x + 3)$ if $x = \frac{1}{3}, 0, -1, -1\frac{1}{2}$.

4. What value of x makes (i) $(x - 5)$ zero, (ii) $(x + 7)$ zero?

5. What value of x satisfies (i) $3x + 1 = 0$, (ii) $2x - 9 = 0$?

State the values of x which satisfy:

6. $(x - 5)(x + 7) = 0$ **7.** $(x + 3)(x + 1) = 0$

8. $(2x + 1)(3x - 5) = 0$ **9.** $x(x - 10) = 0$

Solve the equations:

10. $x^2 - 9x + 20 = 0$ **11.** $x^2 + 5x + 6 = 0$

12. $x^2 = x + 2$ **13.** $x^2 + 5x - 14 = 0$

14. $x^2 - 3x = 0$ **15.** $x^2 - 9 = 0$

16. $6x^2 - 5x + 1 = 0$ **17.** $2x^2 + x - 3 = 0$

18. $3x^2 - 5x + 2 = 0$ **19.** $5x^2 + 4x = 0$

20. $4x^2 - 25 = 0$ **21.** $4x^2 + 8x + 3 = 0$

22. $5x^2 = 3x + 2$ **23.** $7x^2 - 8x + 1 = 0$

24. $x(2x + 3) = 2$ **25.** $3 - 11x = 4x^2$

26. $2x(x + 2) + x = 0$ **27.** $4x(x - 1) = 15$

Solve the equations, giving your answers correct to 2 decimal places:

28. $x^2 - 7 = 0$ **29.** $4x^2 = 11$

30. $3x^2 = 2$ **31.** $x = 10/x$

32. $x^2 - 2x - 5 = 0$ **33.** $x^2 - 6x - 11 = 0$

34. $x^2 + 10x + 2 = 0$ **35.** $x^2 - 8x + 2 = 0$

36. $x^2 - 3x + 1 = 0$ **37.** $x^2 + 7x - 10 = 0$

38. $2x^2 + 5x - 9 = 0$ **39.** $3x^2 + 11x + 5 = 0$

40. $5x^2 - 10x - 4 = 0$ **41.** $4x^2 + x - 2 = 0$

42. A rectangle has a length of $(x + 5)$ cm and width of x cm. State its area in square centimetres. If the area is 36 cm², find x.

43. I think of two whole numbers, one being 3 greater than the other. When I square each number and add the results together I get 89. Find the two numbers.

44. The sides of a right-angled triangle are $3x$, $(x + 3)$ and $(4x - 3)$ cm. Write down an equation for x and use it to find the shortest side of the triangle. [Take $(4x - 3)$ cm as the length of the hypotenuse.]

FORMULAE: CONSTRUCTION

EXERCISE 27

1. A boy is now x yr old. How old was he n yr ago?

2. How many minutes are there in y hours?

3. A $\frac{1}{2}$ litre of milk costs x pence. Find the cost of n litres.

4. A car has an average speed of x km/h. How far does it travel in t h and how long does it take to travel n km?

5. A boy can swim the length of a swimming bath in t seconds. How many lengths can he swim in n minutes?

6. I buy x kg of apples at y pence per kg and w kg of pears at z pence per kg. Find the total cost.

7. A rectangular block is x cm long, y cm wide and z cm high. State the total surface area in cm².

8. Mary has x pence and Joan has y pence. Mary gives Joan 5 pence. How much more has Mary than Joan?

9. Find in kilogrammes the total weight of x parcels if their average weight is w grammes.

10. I run for x seconds at a metres per second and walk for y seconds at b metres per second. What is my average speed?

11. If the interest on £100 invested for 1 yr is £x, find the interest on £n invested for t yr at the same rate.

12. A rectangular lawn a metres by b metres is surrounded by a path of width c metres. Calculate the area of the path.

FORMULAE: EVALUATION

EXERCISE 28

Find the value of:

1. $\pi r^2 h$ when $\pi = 3\frac{1}{7}$, $r = 3\frac{1}{2}$, $h = 4$.

2. $\dfrac{\text{PRT}}{100}$ when P $= 375$, R $= 6$, T $= 5$.

3. $u + ft$ when $u = 40$, $f = 32$, $t = 1\frac{1}{2}$.

4. $2\pi rh + \pi r^2$ when $\pi = 3\frac{1}{7}$, $r = 6$, $h = 4$.

5. $\dfrac{p + q}{p + t}$ when $p = 3 \cdot 7$, $q = 0 \cdot 8$, $t = 2 \cdot 3$.

6. $\dfrac{(a - b)(c - d)}{ac - bd}$ when $a = 3$, $b = 1$, $c = 2$, $d = -\frac{2}{3}$.

7. $2\pi \sqrt{\dfrac{l}{g}}$ when $\pi = 3\frac{1}{7}$, $l = 98$, $g = 32$.

8. $\dfrac{mv^2}{rg}$ when $m = 1\frac{1}{2}$, $v = 12$, $r = 3$, $g = 32$.

9. If $s = \frac{1}{2} n (a + l)$, find s when $n = 37$, $a = 4\frac{1}{2}$ and $l = 31\frac{1}{2}$.

10. If $v^2 = u^2 + 2fs$, find v when $u = 9$, $f = 18$, and $s = 4$.

11. If $\frac{1}{v} = \frac{1}{u} + \frac{1}{f}$, find v when $f = 20$ and $u = 30$.

12. A hollow metal tube has an external radius of a cm, an internal radius of b cm and a length of l cm. Find an expression for the volume, v cm³, of the metal. If $a = 2\frac{1}{2}$, $b = 2$, $l = 14$ and $\pi = \frac{22}{7}$, find v.

13. A ball is thrown upwards with a speed of u metres per second. After t seconds its height is h metres where $h = ut - 5t^2$. If $u = 30$, find h for each of the values $t = 1, 2, 4$ and 8. Explain the last two results. What is the greatest height of the ball?

FORMULAE: CHANGE OF SUBJECT

EXERCISE 29

Make x the subject of each of the following formulae:

1. $x + a = b$　　**2.** $x - c = d$　　**3.** $ex = f$

4. $\frac{x}{g} = h$　　　**5.** $kx + m = n$　　**6.** $x^2 = p$

7. $\frac{1}{x} = r$　　　**8.** $\frac{s}{x} = \frac{t}{u}$

Change each formula to make the given letter the subject:

9. $A = lb$; l　　　　　　**10.** $c = \pi d$; d

11. $p = 2l + 2b$; l　　　　**12.** $A + B + C = 180$; B

13. $t = \frac{p}{b}$; p　　　　　**14.** $s = \frac{p}{h}$; h

15. $A = \pi r^2$; r　　　　　**16.** $V = l^3$; l

17. $v = u + ft$; f　　　　**18.** $v^2 = u^2 + 2fs$; s

19. $s = \frac{1}{2}gt^2$; g　　　　**20.** $w = \frac{3bd^2}{4l}$; d

21. $V = \pi r^2 h$; r　　　　**22.** $V = \frac{4}{3}\pi r^3$; r

23. $A = \frac{1}{2}(a + b)h$; h **24.** $\frac{1}{v} + \frac{1}{u} = \frac{1}{f}$; v

25. $A = \frac{1}{2}(a + b)h$; a

26. A square has a side of x cm, a perimeter of p cm and an area of n cm². Express p and n in terms of x. Hence express n in terms of p.

GRAPHS

Exercise 30

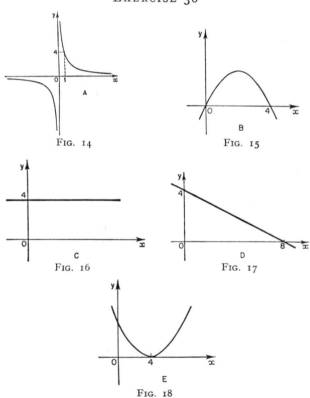

Fig. 14

Fig. 15

Fig. 16

Fig. 17

Fig. 18

1. From the following list, select the equation for each of the above graphs:

$y = x^2 + 4$; $x = 4$; $y = 4$; $y = 4x$; $y = x^2 - 8x + 16$;
$y = 4x - x^2$; $y = \dfrac{4}{x}$; $y = x^4$; $y = 4 - \frac{1}{2}x$; $8x = 4y$

2. *Sketch* the graphs of (i) $y = x$; (ii) $y = x^2$; (iii) $y = \frac{1}{2}x + 3$. If $(4, a)$ and $(b, 1)$ are points on (iii), find a and b.

3. Fig. 19 shows the graph of $y = 6 + x - x^2$.

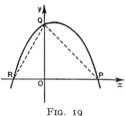

FIG. 19

  (i) State the value of y at Q.
  (ii) Find the value of x at P and at R.
  (iii) Find the gradient of RQ.
  (iv) Find the gradient of QP.

4. A stone falls a distance s metres in time t seconds where $s = 5t^2$. Calculate the values of s for $t = \frac{1}{2}$, 1, 2, 3, 4, $4\frac{1}{2}$, 5. Plot points corresponding to these values using 2 cm to represent 1 second and 1 cm to represent 10 metres. Hence draw the graph of $s = 5t^2$. Use the graph to find:

  (i) the distance a stone falls in $2\frac{1}{2}$ seconds, and
  (ii) the time for a stone to fall 65 metres.

5. Draw the graph of $y = \dfrac{120}{x}$. Take as values of x 10, 15, 20, 30, 40, 50, 60 and use 1 cm to represent 5 units of the x axis and 1 cm to represent 1 unit on the y axis.

From the graph find:

  (i) the time taken for a journey of 120 km at 37 km/h,
  (ii) the speed required to travel 120 km in $4\frac{1}{2}$ h.

6. Draw the graphs of $y = x + 2$ and $3y = 3 - 2x$ from $x = -3$ to $x = +3$.

  (i) Use the graph to find a pair of values of x and y which satisfy both $y = x + 2$ and $3y + 2x = 3$.

(ii) Shade the region in which $y < x + 2$, $y > 1 - \frac{2}{3}x$ and $x < \frac{1}{2}$. What is the greatest value of y in this region?

7. For values of x from -3 to $+3$, draw the graphs of $y = \frac{1}{2}x^2$ (A) and $y = x + 1\frac{1}{2}$ (B).

Complete the following:

(i) The point $(2\cdot4, 3\cdot9)$ is on graph .....

(ii) The point $(1\cdot2, ...)$ is on graph A.

(iii) The graphs intersect at $(...., ...)$ and $(...., ...)$.

(iv) At the points of intersection, the values of x are the solutions of the equation $x^2 - .... - .... = 0$.

8. Draw the graph of $y = x^2$. Use 2 cm for 1 unit on the x axis and 1 cm for 1 unit on the y axis; take values of x from -3 to $+3$.

Using the same axes plot the graphs of $y = 3 - x$ and $y = \frac{1}{3}x + 6$. State the solutions to (i) $x^2 + x - 3 = 0$ and (ii) $2x^2 - x - 12 = 0$.

Use the graph of $y = x^2$ to find approximate values for $1\cdot8^2$ and $\sqrt{3}$.

9. Draw the graph of $y = 2^x$ from $x = 0$ to $x = 6$ taking 2 cm for 1 unit on the x axis and 1 cm for 5 units on the y axis. In addition to points for which x is a whole number, use the points $(3\cdot5, 11\cdot3)$, $(4\cdot5, 22\cdot6)$, $(5\cdot5, 45\cdot2)$.

Draw also the graph of $y = 10x - 20$ from $x = 2$ to $x = 6$. For what values of x is $10(x - 2) > 2^x$?

10. Draw the graph of $y = x(4 - x)$ from $x = -1$ to 5 using 2 cm to 1 unit on each axis.

(i) What is the maximum value of y?

(ii) What is the value of y when $x = 2\cdot8$?

(iii) For what range of values of x is $y > 2$?

(iv) Solve the equation $x^2 - 4x + 2 = 0$.

(v) What can you say about the equation $x(4 - x) = 6$ and $x(4 - x) = -6$?

INEQUALITIES

State the values of x for which:

1. $x + 9 > 12$ **2.** $2x - 3 > 6$ **3.** $3x + 4 < 21$

4. $2x + 7 < 1$ **5.** $5 - 4x < 11$ **6.** $2 - \frac{1}{2}x > 5$

7. $13 \geqslant x + 2 \geqslant 10 - x$

State the integral values of x for which:

8. $2x - 5 > 4$ **9.** $10 - 5x > 22$ **10.** $2 + 3x > 100$

11. $9 - x < x < 25 - 2x$ **12.** $x - 3 > 5x > 3x - 11$

State whether the expression is positive or negative when x satisfies the given condition:

13. $3x - 11$: (i) $x > 4$, (ii) x is negative.

14. $5 - 2x$: (i) $x > 3$, (ii) $x < 2$.

15. $(x - 3)(x - 7)$: (i) $x > 7$, (ii) $x < 3$, (iii) $7 > x > 3$.

16. $(x + 2)(x + 5)$: (i) $x > -2$, (ii) $x < -5$, (iii) $-2 > x > -5$.

17. $(x + 4)(x - 2)$: (i) $x > 2$, (ii) $x < -4$, (iii) $2 > x > -4$.

18. $(3x - 1)(5 - 2x)$: (i) $x < \frac{1}{3}$, (ii) $x > 2\frac{1}{2}$, (iii) $2\frac{1}{2} > x > \frac{1}{3}$.

19. $F = (x + 1)(x - 4)$. For what values of x is F negative?

20. $G = (2x - 1)(3x + 1)$. For what values of x is G positive?

21. $H = (5 - y)(y + 11)$. For what values of y is H positive?

22. $K = (7 + 2m)(m + 1)$. For what values of m is K negative?

23. Correct the signs in the following statements, where necessary:

   (i) $6 \cdot 25 > 6 \cdot 5$;   (ii) $-5 < 2$;   (iii) $-3 = 3$;
   (iv) $0 < -0 \cdot 8$;   (v) $(0 \cdot 5)^2 < 0 \cdot 5$.

24. Combine into a single statement $x + 7 > 4$ and $1 + x < 6$.

25. $P = 3x - 5$. What is the smallest integral value of x for which (i) $P > 0$; (ii) $P > 8$?

26. $Q = 2y - 7$. What is the largest integral value of y for which (i) $Q < 0$; (ii) $Q < 5\cdot5$?

27. Find the smallest integral value of x for which (i) $x^2 > 20$; (ii) $x^3 > 20$.

28. Complete: If $a = x^2$ and $b = 3x + 7$, $a > b$ if $x = $ ..... (Smallest positive integer.)

29. Complete: If the area of a square of side x m is A m² and the perimeter is p m, A $> p$ if $x > $ .... .

30. Find pairs of positive integral values of x and y for which $2x + 3y < 10$.

31. Find pairs of positive integral values of a and b less than 5 for which $10 > 5a - 3b > 5$.

32. Sketch the graphs of $y = 3$, $x = 2$ and $y = x$. Shade the region for which $x < y < 3$ and $0 < x < 2$.

33. Sketch the graphs of $y = x^2$ and $y = x + 3$. Shade the region for which x is negative, $y < x + 3$ and $y > x^2$.

34. Sketch the graphs of $y = 2x - 1$ and $y = x + 2$. Shade the region for which $x + 2 > y > 2x - 1$ and y is positive. What is the greatest value of y satisfying this condition?

INDICES

EXERCISE 32

Simplify:

1. $a^5 \times a^2$ **2.** $a^5 \div a^2$ **3.** $(a^5)^2$ **4.** $b^3 \times b^6$

5. $c^9 \div c^3$ **6.** $(d^2)^3$ **7.** $e^4 \times e$ **8.** $f^8 \div f$

9. $g^3 \times g \times g^2$ **10.** $(h^5 \times h^2) \div h^3$ **11.** $\sqrt[2]{(j^{10})}$

12. $\sqrt[3]{(k^{12})}$ **13.** $\dfrac{m^{10}}{m^2}$ **14.** $\dfrac{p^{12}}{p^3}$

15. $t^2 \div t^5$ **16.** $x^4 \div x^6$

Find the value of:

17. 3^3 **18.** 2^4 **19.** 10^3 **20.** 5^3

21. $7^6 \div 7^4$ **22.** $2^{20} \div 2^{17}$

Simplify:

23. $a^x \times a^{3x}$ **24.** $b^{2y} \times b^{4y}$ **25.** $(c^z)^3$ **26.** $d^{3x} \div d^{5x}$

27. $f^{2x} \times f^x \div f^{4x}$ **28.** $g^y \times g^y \times g^x$

29. Find the value of x (i) if $2^x = 64$, (ii) if $3^x = 243$.

30. Find the square of 2×3^2 (i) in index form, (ii) without indices.

31. Find the cube of $2^2 \times 3$ (i) in index form, (ii) without indices.

32. Find the square of $2^4 \times 5^2$ (i) in index form, (ii) without indices.

33. Find the square root of $2^4 \times 3^2$ (i) in index form, (ii) without indices.

Find the value of:

34. 10^2 **35.** 10^{-2} **36.** 10^4 **37.** 10^{-3}

Give as a power of 10:

38. 100,000   **39.** $\frac{1}{10}$ **40.** 1 million   **41.** 0·00001

Express as single numbers (i.e. without powers of 10):

42. $4·7 \times 10^2$ **43.** $5·8 \times 10^4$ **44.** 6×10^3

45. $3·429 \times 10^2$ **46.** $3·2 \times 10^{-2}$ **47.** $8·7 \times 10^{-4}$

48. 5×10^{-3} **49.** $4·012 \times 10^{-1}$

Write in standard form (i.e. as $A \times 10^n$ where $0 < A < 10$):

50. 294   **51.** 75,320   **52.** 230·4   **53.** 36·42

54. 0·056   **55.** 0·0007   **56.** 0·00503   **57.** 0·963

58. 23 billion   **59.** 16 thousandths

60. 229 million kilometres, the distance of Mars from the Sun.

61. The number of centimetres in 50 kilometres.

62. The area of the surface of the Earth, 365 million square kilometres.

63. The distance travelled by light in 1 hour, given that its speed is 300 000 kilometres per second.

ANGLES

Angles at a point; angles on a straight line; angles made with parallel lines.

EXERCISE 33

1. Direction A is WNW.

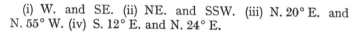

Fig. 20

(i) Name directions B, C and D.
(ii) What is the size of the angle turned through in the clockwise direction (*a*) from N to C, (*b*) from N to B, (*c*) from B to C, (*d*) from D to A.

2. Draw a figure to show each pair of compass directions and state the smaller angle between them:

(i) W. and SE. (ii) NE. and SSW. (iii) N. 20° E. and N. 55° W. (iv) S. 12° E. and N. 24° E.

3. I face N. 30° W. What direction shall I be facing after turning through (i) 60° anticlockwise, (ii) a right-angle anticlockwise, (iii) 180° clockwise, (iv) 250° clockwise?

4. Through what angle does the minute hand of a clock turn in (i) a quarter of an hour, (ii) 20 minutes?

5. Through what angle does the hour hand of a clock turn in (i) 7 hours, (ii) half an hour?

6. Through what angle does the earth turn in (i) 1 h, (ii) 5 h 20 min?

7. (i) If *a* = 40° and *b* = 60°, find *c*.
(ii) If *b* = 75° and *c* = 2*a*, find *a*.
(iii) If *a* = *b* = 2*c*, find *a*.

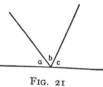

Fig. 21

48

8. [Fig. 22] (i) If $d = 120°$, $e = 80°$ and $f = 45°$, find g.
  (ii) If $d = 130°$, $g = 150°$ and $e = 3f$, find f.
  (iii) If $f = 36°$ and $d = e = f$, find d.

9. In Fig. 22, let the four lines meet at O. What follows (i) if $d + e = 180$, (ii) if $d = f$ and $e = g$?

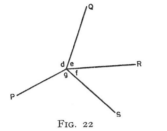

Fig. 22   Fig. 23

10. In Fig. 23 name:

  (i) a pair of vertically opposite angles,
  (ii) a pair of corresponding angles,
  (iii) a pair of alternate angles,
  (iv) If $b = 115°$, find d.

Find the unknown marked angles:

11.

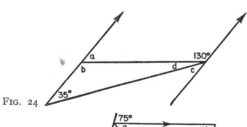

Fig. 24

12.

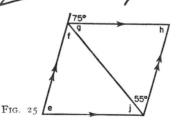

Fig. 25

13.   **14.**

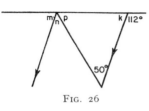

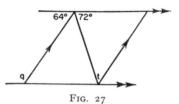

Fig. 26   Fig. 27

15. Copy Fig. 28, and mark on it as many angles as you can calculate.

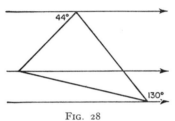

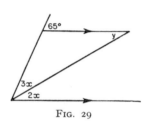

Fig. 28   Fig. 29

16. In Fig. 29, find x and y.

TRIANGLES AND POLYGONS

Angle-sum of triangle; exterior angle of triangle; isosceles triangle; equilateral triangle; regular polygon.

EXERCISE 34

1. Find the third angle of a triangle having angles of (i) 64° and 78°; (ii) 48° and 105°.

2. Is it possible to have a triangle with angles of (i) 80°, 50°, 60°; (ii) 45°, 62°, 53°; (iii) 34°, 76°, 70°; (iv) 103°, 39°, 48°?

Questions 3 to 8. Use Fig. 30.

3. If $x = z$ and $y = 80°$, find x.

4. If $x + y = z$, find z.

5. If AB = CA and $y = 52°$, find x.

6. If AB = BC = CA, find x.

7. If $w = 130°$ and $x = 75°$, find y.

8. If $w = 125°$ and AB = AC, find x.

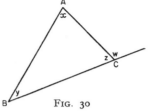

FIG. 30

9. Calculate the exterior angle of a regular polygon having (i) 8 sides; (ii) 12 sides; (iii) 20 sides.

10. Calculate the interior angle of a regular polygon having (i) 10 sides; (ii) 9 sides; (iii) 16 sides.

11. Is it possible to have a regular polygon with an exterior angle of (i) 40°; (ii) 50°; (iii) 24°?

Where it is possible, state the number of sides.

12. Is it possible to have a regular polygon with an interior angle of (i) 100°; (ii) 160°; (iii) 145°?

Where it is possible, state the number of sides.

13. An isosceles triangle has one angle of 104°. Find the other two angles.

14. The angles of a triangle are $2x°$, $3x°$ and $4x°$. Find x.

15. The angles of a quadrilateral are $3y°$, $3y°$, $4y°$ and $5y°$. Find y.

Questions 16 to 22.

Calculate the sizes of a, b, c, etc:

16.   **17.**

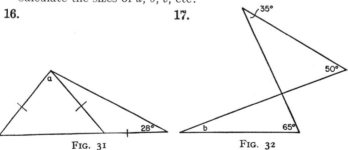

FIG. 31   FIG. 32

18.

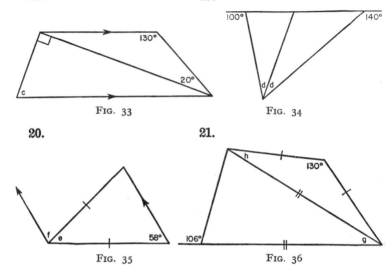

Fig. 33

19.

Fig. 34

20.

Fig. 35

21.

Fig. 36

22.

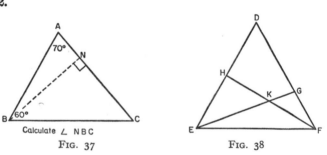

Calculate ∠ N B C

Fig. 37

Fig. 38

23. [Fig. 38.] △DEF is equilateral; ∠DEG is 38° and ∠DFH is 25°. Calculate the angles of △EKF.

24. [Fig. 39.] PQ = QR = RP = PS and ∠SPR = 90°. Calculate ∠PRS, ∠SRQ and ∠SQP. Why is SQ = ST?

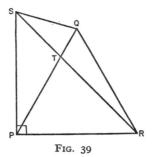

Fig. 39

25. ABCD is a regular pentagon. Calculate the angles of △ABD. If AC and BD intersect at H, calculate ∠AHB.

26. Equilateral triangle PQT is drawn inside square PQRS. Calculate ∠PTS and ∠STR.

QUADRILATERALS

Exercise 35

A: Parallelogram   D: Square
B: Rhombus   E: Isosceles trapezium
C: Rectangle   F: Kite

1. Sketch the six quadrilaterals named above and show any axes of symmetry by means of dotted lines.

Questions 2, 3 and 4: consider each of the statements and state for which of the above quadrilaterals it is true:

2. (i) Both pairs of opposite sides are equal.
    (ii) All four sides are equal.
    (iii) One, and only one, pair of opposite sides are parallel.

3. (i) Both pairs of opposite angles are equal.
    (ii) One, and only one, pair of opposite angles are equal.
    (iii) All angles are 90°.

4. (i) The diagonals are equal.
    (ii) The diagonals are perpendicular.

    (iii) The diagonals do *not* bisect each other.
    (iv) The angles at the vertices are bisected by the diagonals.

5. Show that the four angles of a quadrilateral add up to 360°.

6. State the nature of quadrilateral ABCD if:

    (i) $\angle A = \angle B = \angle C = \angle D$.
    (ii) $\angle A = \angle B$ and $\angle C = \angle D$.
    (iii) $\angle A = \angle C$ and $\angle B = \angle D$.
    (iv) AB = BC and CD = DA.

7. PQRS is a parallelogram. What special kind of parallelogram is obtained if:

    (i) PR = QS?
    (ii) PR is perpendicular to QS?
    (iii) PR = QS *and* PR is perpendicular to QS?

8. [Fig. 40.] Diagonals AC and BD of square ABCD meet at P. BQ = BP. Calculate the angles of △PCQ.

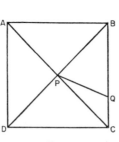

FIG. 40

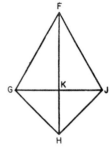

FIG. 41

9. The diagonals PR and QS of rhombus PQRS intersect at O; $\angle PQR = 68°$. Calculate $\angle QPO$.

10. Fig. 41 shows a kite and its diagonals. △FGJ is equilateral and KH = KG. Calculate $\angle GHJ$ and $\angle FGH$.

CONSTRUCTIONS

Bisection of angles and straight lines; perpendiculars to given lines and angles equal to given angles; angles of 60°, 30°, 90° and 45°; triangles and quadrilaterals; proportional division of a straight line; polygons inscribed in circles.

EXERCISE 36

Do NOT use a protractor in Questions 1 to 6.

1. Draw $\triangle$ABC given that AB = 8 cm, BC = 7 cm and $\angle$B = 60°. Construct the bisectors of the three angles of the triangle. Let the bisector of $\angle$A meet BC at P. Measure AP.

2. Draw $\triangle$GHK having GH = 5 cm, GK = 6 cm and $\angle$HGK = 120°. Construct the perpendicular bisectors of GH and GK. Let them meet at L. Measure LG. With centre L and radius LG draw an arc of a circle to pass through G, H and K.

3. Construct $\triangle$PQR given that PQ = 8 cm, QR = 9 cm and RP = 7·5 cm. Construct the three altitudes of the triangle and measure them.

4. Draw $\triangle$ DEF having DE = 4·6 cm, EF = 5·6 cm and FD = 3·8 cm. Construct $\triangle$XYZ having $\angle$Y = $\angle$E, $\angle$Z = $\angle$F and YZ = 4·6 cm. Measure XY.

5. Draw $\triangle$ABC having AC = BC = 6 cm and AB = 4 cm. Through A construct AD parallel to BC and from C construct a line perpendicular to AD and meeting AD at E. Measure CE.

6. Construct angles of 30°, 45° and 15°.

7. Draw a line of length 82 mm and divide it into five equal parts.

8. Draw a line AB of length 9·8 cm. Find a point P on AB such that AP : PB = 4 : 3. Measure AP.

9. Construct quad. PQRS having PQ = 4 cm, QR = 7 cm, $\angle$R = 60° and $\angle$Q = $\angle$S = 90°. Construct T, the mid-point of PR. With centre T draw a circle to pass through the vertices of the quadrilateral.

10. Draw a circle of radius 5 cm. Construct a regular hexagon having its six vertices on the circle.

11. Draw a circle of radius 4 cm. Construct a regular octagon having its eight vertices on the circle. Measure a side.

12. Construct the trapezium HKLM in which HK is parallel to ML, HK = 4 cm, KL = 6 cm, LM = 8 cm and ∠HKL = 120°. Construct the perpendicular from H to ML and measure it.

13. Construct as many *non*-congruent triangles as possible having sides of 7 cm and 5 cm and an angle of 50°.

SIMILARITY

EXERCISE 37

1. Calculate *a* and *b*.

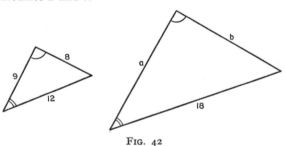

FIG. 42

2. Calculate *c* and *d*.

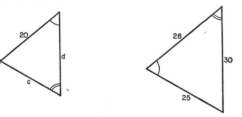

FIG. 43

3. Calculate *f*, *g* and *h*. (Use Pythagoras' Theorem)

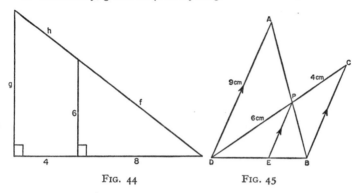

FIG. 44   FIG. 45

4. [Fig. 45.] Name (i) a triangle similar to △ADP, (ii) a triangle similar to △DBC. Calculate (i) BC, (ii) PE.

5. A pole of height 3 m has a shadow of length 4 m and at the same moment a tower has a shadow of length 18 m. Calculate the height of the tower.

6. The two sides of a stepladder are 3 m long. A cord of length 1·2 m joins points on the two sides 1 m from the base. Calculate the distance between the feet of the ladder.

7. Copy Fig. 46 and mark equal angles. Calculate AN, CN and AC.

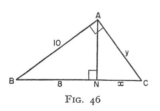

FIG. 46

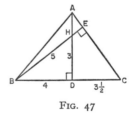

FIG. 47

8. Copy Fig. 47 and mark equal angles. Name three triangles similar to △BHD. Calculate EC and AH.

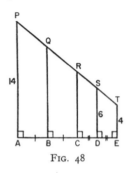

FIG. 48

9. [Fig. 48.] AB = BC and CD = DE. Calculate CR and BQ. If AE = 15, calculate AB.

10. Two circular discs of the same thickness have radii of 10 cm and 6 cm. If the first weighs 225 g, find the weight of the second.

11. Two similar triangles have corresponding sides of 9 cm and 6 cm. If the first has an area of 18 cm², find the area of the second.

12. A spherical soap bubble is blown out until its diameter is doubled. What is the change in (i) its surface area, (ii) its volume and (iii) the thickness of the soap film?

13. Two jugs have the same shape. One is 16 cm high and the other is 12 cm high. If the first holds 1 920 cm³, how much does the second hold?

14. On a '1 cm to 1 km' map, a lake has an area of 1·6 cm². What is its area on (i) a '2 cm to 1 km' map and (ii) a '5 cm to 1 km' map?

15. In △ABC, ∠A = 58°, ∠B = 52°; in △DEF, ∠D = 58°, ∠E = 74°; in △HJK, ∠H = 48°, ∠J = 74°. Which triangles are similar? Write down the ratio statement for corresponding sides.

16. [Fig. 49.] Complete: $\dfrac{AP}{} = \dfrac{}{AC} = \dfrac{PQ}{}$.

If AP = 6 cm, PB = 4 cm and BC = 12 cm, find PQ.

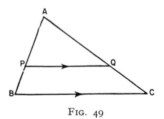

FIG. 49

17. [Fig. 50.] The base, B, for an athletics cup is to be formed by slicing the top part, A, from a cone.

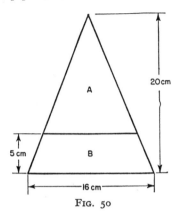

FIG. 50

(i) Find the radius of the top of B.
(ii) Find the ratio of the area of the top of B to the area of its base.
(iii) If the volume of the original cone is 1 340 cm³ approximately, find the volume of B.

CONGRUENCY

EXERCISE 38

1. △DEF is congruent to △ABC and △HJK is similar to △ABC. State the sizes of as many sides and angles as possible.

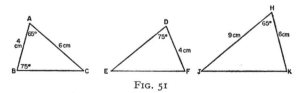

FIG. 51

2. By making freehand sketches, find which of the following triangles are congruent:

    △LMN: ∠L = 43°, LM = 5 cm, LN = 6 cm.
    △PQR: ∠P = 43°, QR = 5 cm, PQ = 6 cm.
    △XYZ: ∠Y = 43°, XY = 5 cm, YZ = 6 cm.

3. By making freehand sketches, find which of the following triangles are congruent:

    △DEF: ∠D = 54°, ∠E = 77°, DE = 8 cm.
    △GHJ: ∠G = 54°, ∠H = 49°, GH = 8 cm.
    △STV: ∠V = 77°, ∠T = 54°, SV = 8 cm.
    △XYZ: ∠X = 49°, ∠Z = 77°, YZ = 8 cm.

4. In △s ABC and PQR, ∠A = ∠R, ∠C = ∠P and BC = PQ. Name the other pairs of equal sides.

5. In △s DEF and XYZ, ∠F = ∠Z, EF = XZ and DF = YZ. Name the other pairs of equal angles.

6. Fig. 52 shows sketches of four triangles. (i) Which triangle is congruent to △I? (ii) Which is similar to △I?

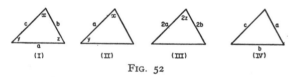

FIG. 52

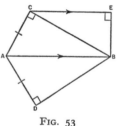

FIG. 53

7. [Fig. 53] (i) Which triangle is congruent to △ABC?
    (ii) Which triangle is similar to △ABC?

8. AM is a median of △ABC; BP and CQ are perpendiculars from B and C to AM which is produced. Prove that BP = CQ.

9. In △PQR, ∠P is acute. Squares PQVW and PRXY are drawn outside △PQR. Prove that RW = QY.

SYMMETRY

EXERCISE 39

1. Draw the block capital letters of the alphabet which have axes of symmetry. Show the axes with dotted lines. Which letters have two axes?

2. Draw the block capital letters of the alphabet which have point symmetry. Mark each point of symmetry with a cross.

3. Draw the following and show their axes of symmetry with dotted lines: an isosceles triangle, an equilateral triangle, a square, a rectangle, a rhombus (diamond), a heart, a regular pentagon (5 sides) and a regular hexagon (6 sides).

4. Draw any of the figures of Question 3 which have point symmetry, marking each point with a cross.

5. Copy the following figures. Add lines where necessary so that each has rotational symmetry. State the angle of rotation for each. Which figure has no line of symmetry?

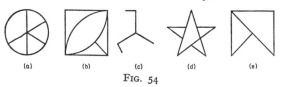

(a) (b) (c) (d) (e)

FIG. 54

6. State the number of axes of symmetry of each of the following solids: a sharpened pencil, a cone, a sphere, an egg, a cube and a tetrahedron.

SCALE DRAWING

EXERCISE 40

1. Village A is 6 km south of village B. From A the bearing of castle C is N. 65° E. and from B it is S. 72° E. Find the distance of C from A.

2. A harbour is 6 nautical miles SW. of a lighthouse. A ship leaves the harbour and steams due east. After 45 minutes the bearing of the lighthouse from the ship is N. 15° W. Find the speed of the ship in knots.

3. London is 225 km due south of Grimsby and Derby is 120 km from Grimsby in the direction S. 52° W. Find the distance and bearing of Derby from London.

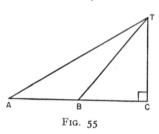

FIG. 55

4. [Fig. 55.] CT is a tower and BC is a river. From A and B the angles of elevation of T are 41° and 65°. If AB is 45 m, how high is the tower and how wide is the river?

5. From a point P, a radar fix on a ship is given by its distance x nautical miles and its true bearing $\theta°$ and the position is described as $(x, \theta°)$. A radar fix on a ship is (8, 20°) at 3 p.m. and (11, 320°) at 4 p.m. Find the speed of the ship and the direction in which it is travelling.

6. A ship steams at 18 knots on a course of S. 20° E. for $1\frac{1}{2}$ h then at 16 knots on a course of N. 76° E. for $\frac{1}{2}$ h and then at 10 knots for 1 h on a course of N. 12° W. Find its bearing and distance from its starting point.

7. From a base line AB on the bank of a river, a point C is observed on the opposite bank. $\angle ABC = 62°$ and $\angle BAC = 44°$. If AB = 70 m, find the width of the river.

PYTHAGORAS' THEOREM

EXERCISE 41

1. If $\theta = 90°$, $b = 8$, $c = 6$, find a.

2. If $\theta = 90°$, $b = 24$, $c = 7$, find a.

3. If $\theta = 90°$, $a = 13$, $b = 5$, find c.

4. If $\theta = 90°$, $a = 17$, $c = 8$, find b.

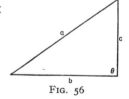

FIG. 56

5. If $a = 12$, $b = 9$, $c = 7$, is θ acute, obtuse or 90°?

6. If $a = 9$, $b = 7$, $c = 6$, is θ acute, obtuse or 90°?

7. If $a = 29$, $b = 21$, $c = 20$, is θ acute, obtuse or 90°?

8. $\triangle$I has sides of 4, 5, and 7; $\triangle$II has sides of 5, 7 and 9; $\triangle$III has sides of 9, 11 and 14. Which triangles have obtuse angles?

9. A rhombus has sides of length 15 cm and one diagonal of length 18 cm. Find the length of the other diagonal.

10. A ladder of length 6·5 m is placed with its foot 2·5 m from a wall. How far up the wall does it reach?

Questions 11 to 15: Find x.

11. **12.** **13.**

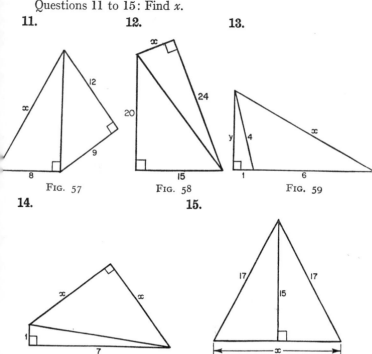

FIG. 57   FIG. 58   FIG. 59

14. **15.**

FIG. 60   FIG. 61

16. In Fig. 56, if $b = 5$ and $c = 7$, calculate a, correct to 2 sig. fig.

17. In Fig. 56, if $a = 9$ and $c = 5$, calculate b, correct to 2 sig. fig.

18. Calculate, correct to 2 sig. fig., the length of a diagonal of a square of side 5 cm.

19. A rectangular field is 45 m wide and has a diagonal of 80 m. Calculate the length of the field, correct to the nearest metre.

20. The lengths of the edges of a rectangular box are 20 cm, 30 cm and 60 cm. Calculate the length of the longest stick which will fit into the box.

21. A football pitch is marked out in a field. To check the right-angles the two diagonals are measured. If the sides of the pitch are 110 m and 70 m, what should be the length of each diagonal?

22. Find two whole numbers, x and y, such that $x^2 + y^2 = 13$. Hence find two even numbers, b and c, such that $b^2 + c^2 = 52$. By using a right-angled triangle construct a line of length $\sqrt{52}$ cm.

23. By using a right-angled triangle construct a line of length $\sqrt{74}$ cm.

SINE, COSINE AND TANGENT

EXERCISE 42

Questions 1 to 6: Use Fig. 62.

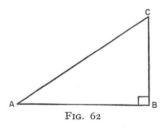

FIG. 62

1. If AB = 6 cm and $\angle$A = 38°, calculate BC.

2. If AB = 8 cm and BC = 5 cm, calculate $\angle$A.

3. If AC = 10 cm and $\angle$A = 62°, calculate BC.

4. If AC = 4 cm and $\angle$A = 20°, calculate AB.

5. If AC = 5 cm and BC = 3 cm, calculate ∠A.

6. If AC = 9 cm and AB = 7 cm, calculate ∠A.

7. From the top of a cliff 120 m high, the angle of depression of a boat is 33° 36′. Calculate the distance of the boat from the cliff.

8. A man 60 m from a tower measures the angle of elevation of the top as 28°. Find the height of the tower.

9. Q is 4 km east of P and R is 6 km south of Q. Calculate the bearing of R from P.

10. The diagonals of a rhombus have lengths of 16 cm and 12 cm. Calculate the acute angle of the rhombus.

11. I walk 80 m along a road which has a gradient of 6°. Find the increase in my height.

12. Calculate the length of the shadow (on horizontal ground) of a vertical post of height 4m when the angle of elevation of the sun is 35°.

13. In △DEF, DE = 5 cm, EF = 12 cm and ∠E = 90°. Calculate DF, tan D and sin F.

14. If cos A = $\frac{3}{5}$ find, without referring to tables, the values of sin A and tan A.

15. A triangle has sides of 47 mm and 59 mm and an angle of 90° between them. Calculate the smallest angle of the triangle.

16. An isosceles triangle has two sides of 6 cm and an angle of 56° between them. Calculate the third side.

17. The sides of a rectangle are 8 cm and 10 cm. Calculate the obtuse angle between the diagonals.

18. A ladder of length 6 m is placed with its base 2 m from the wall. Find the angle it makes with the ground. If the base is moved 1 m farther from the wall, find, correct to the nearest centimetre, the distance moved at the top.

19. A pendulum of length 2 m is attached to a point 3 m from the floor. It swings through 35° each side of the vertical. Calculate its height from the floor at the ends of its swing.

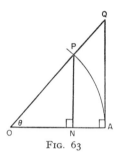

FIG. 63

20. [Fig. 63.] AP is an arc of a circle, centre O, and OPQ is a straight line.

Write down (i) two expressions for tan θ, (ii) two expressions for sin θ.

Construct this figure making OA = 5 cm and $\theta = 32°$. Use your figure to find approximate values for tan 32° and sin 32°.

21. [Fig. 64.] AB = 8 cm, AC = 12 cm and $\angle A = 34°$. Find BD, CE and the area of quad. BCED.

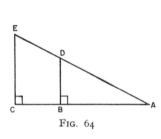

FIG. 64

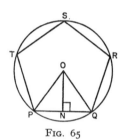

FIG. 65

22. Fig. 65 shows a regular pentagon in a circle of radius 10 cm. Calculate $\angle$POQ, ON, PQ and the area of the pentagon.

23. B is due east of A. The bearing of P from A is S. 34° E. and P is 530 m SW. of B. Q is due north of P and on the line AB. Find PQ, AQ and AB.

24. From a coastguard station 120 m above sea level the angles of depression of two boats are 25° and 50°. Find the distance between the boats.

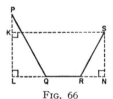

FIG. 66

25. Fig. 66 shows the section of a railway cutting. PQ = 28 m, QR = 10 m, RS = 20 m, $\angle$PQL = 55° and $\angle$SRN = 45°. Calculate LQ, RN, PK and $\angle$PSK.

LOCI

1. Sketch the locus of point P in each of the following cases. Use a dotted line for the locus and describe it in words:

   (i) P is 1 cm from a fixed straight line of indefinite length.

  (ii) P is 2 cm from a fixed point A.

 (iii) P is equidistant from two fixed points B and C.

 (iv) P is equidistant from two fixed straight lines DE and DF.

2. Sketch the following loci:

   (i) The centre of a five pence coin rolling with its edge in contact with the edge of a fixed ten pence coin.

  (ii) The centre of a ladder which slides so that one end is in contact with the ground and the other with a wall.

 (iii) A spot of white paint on the tyre of a bicycle wheel.

3. What surface is traced out by:

   (i) The edge AB of a postcard ABCD which is rotating about edge CD.

  (ii) The hypotenuse PQ of a set square PQR which is rotating about PR.

 (iii) The circumference of a circular hoop which is rotating about a diameter.

4. Draw $\triangle$ABC having AB = 8 cm, BC = 6 cm, CA = 7 cm. Construct (i) the locus of points equidistant from B and C, and (ii) the locus of points 3 cm from the mid-point of AB. Mark as K and L the points on both loci and measure KL.

5. Draw $\triangle$PQR having PQ = 9 cm, QR = 6·6 cm, RP = 7·8 cm. Construct (i) the locus of points equidistant from RP and QP, and (ii) the locus of points 3 cm from RQ. Mark two points, X and Y, satisfying both conditions and measure XY.

6. B is 220 m due east of A; C is north-east of A and 180 m from B. Draw a scale diagram to show two possible positions of C. How far are they from A?

7. Draw △DEF having DE = 7 cm, EF = 8 cm and ∠DEF = 60°. Construct (i) the locus of points equidistant from D and E, (ii) the locus of points equidistant from E and F and (iii) the locus of points equidistant from F and D. Shade the part of the triangle containing points which are nearer to D than to E and F. Draw the circumcircle of the triangle and measure its radius.

8. Draw △PQR having PQ = 9 cm, QR = 8 cm and RP = 7 cm. Construct the incircle of the triangle and measure its radius.

ANGLE PROPERTIES OF CIRCLES

EXERCISE 44

1. In Fig. 67, AB is a diameter, O is the centre, AC is a tangent and M is the mid-point of chord EF.

  (i) State the sizes of the angles OMF, ADB and CAB. Give reasons.
  (ii) If t = 65°, find s and u.

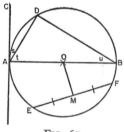

FIG. 67

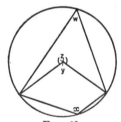

FIG. 68

2. Fig. 68 shows a cyclic quadrilateral and two radii.
  (i) Which angle is twice w? Give a reason.
  (ii) Which angle is twice x?

(iii) What is the connection between w and x?

(iv) If $w = 65°$, find x and z.

3. [Fig. 69.] The point at which AD and CB intersect is NOT the centre of the circle.

If $a = 55°$ and $b = 42°$, find c, d and e. Give reasons.

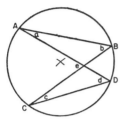

FIG. 69

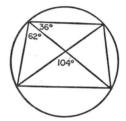

FIG. 70

4. In Fig. 68, if $y = 140°$, find x.

5. In Fig. 69, if $e = 80°$ and $a = 32°$, find d.

6. In Fig. 69, if AB is parallel to CD and $a = 35°$, find e.

7. Copy Fig. 70 and fill in the sizes of the remaining angles.

8. Fig. 71. Find the sizes of as many angles as possible.

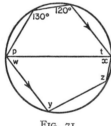

FIG. 71

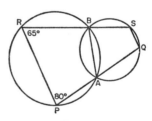

FIG. 72

9. In Fig. 72, PAQ and RBS are straight lines. Calculate $\angle$AQS. What follows for PR and QS?

10. The sides AB and DC of cyclic quadrilateral ABCD are produced to meet at X. $\angle$AXD $= 38°$ and $\angle$BCX $= 66°$. Find $\angle$CBA and $\angle$ADC, giving reasons.

11. Calculate all the angles in Fig. 73.

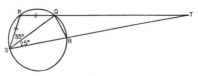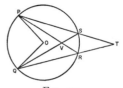

FIG. 73　　　　　FIG. 74

12. In Fig. 74, O is the centre of the circle; chords PR and QS intersect at V; chords PS and QR are produced to meet at T. If $\angle POQ = 96°$ and $\angle PTQ = 36°$, find $\angle PSQ$, $\angle VQR$ and $\angle SVR$.

13. Draw a circle having AB as a diameter and CD as a chord parallel to AB. Join AC, AD and BD. Take $\angle ADC = 28°$ and calculate all the other angles in the figure.

14. In Fig. 75, AOB is a diameter. Find p, q, r and s.

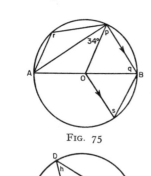

FIG. 75

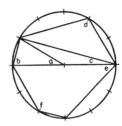

FIG. 76

15. In Fig. 76, the twelve points on the circumference are equally spaced. Calculate a, b, c, d, e and f.

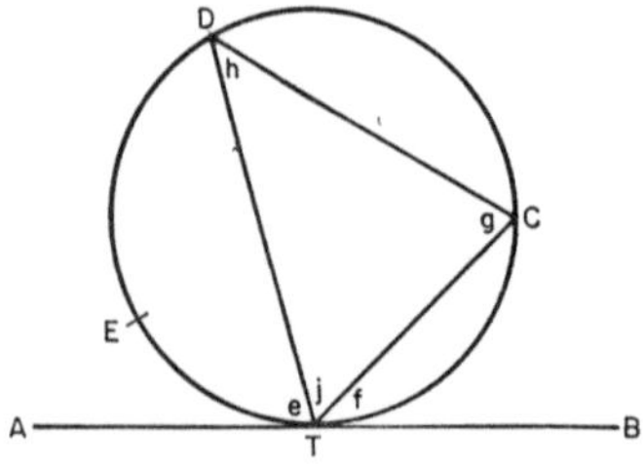

16. In Fig. 77, AB is a tangent.

　　(i) Name an angle equal to e.

　　(ii) Name an angle equal to f.

FIG. 77

(iii) If $e = 75°$ and $f = 55°$, calculate $\angle$TCD, $\angle$TED and $\angle$TEC.

17. In Fig. 78, O is the centre and AB is a tangent. Find a, b and c.

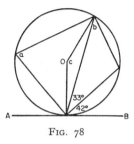

FIG. 78

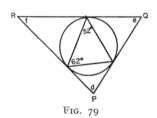

FIG. 79

18. In Fig. 79, PQ, QR and RP are tangents. Calculate d, e and f.

CHORDS, TANGENTS, ARCS AND SECTORS

EXERCISE 45

1. If AB $= 12$ cm and ON $= 8$ cm, calculate AO and $\angle$AOB.

2. If AO $= 17$ cm and ON $= 15$ cm, calculate AB and $\angle$OAB.

3. CD and EF are parallel chords in a circle of radius 5 cm. If CD $= 6$ cm and EF $= 8$ cm, calculate the distance between them when they are (i) on the same side of the centre, (ii) on opposite sides of the centre.

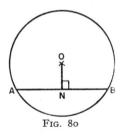

FIG. 80

4. A circle passes through the four corners of a rectangle of length 6 cm and width 2·5 cm. Calculate the diameter of the circle.

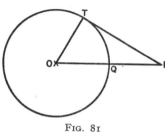

FIG. 81

In Fig. 81, O is the centre, OQP is a straight line and PT is a tangent.

5. If OQ = 5 cm and QP = 8 cm, calculate TP.

6. If OT = 4 cm and OP = 6 cm, calculate PT, correct to 3 sig. fig., and ∠TOP.

7. Fig. 82. If radius AO is 6 cm, calculate ∠AOB, ∠AON and AB.

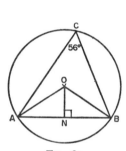

FIG. 82

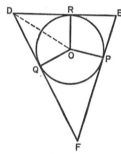

FIG. 83

8. In Fig. 83, DE, EF and FD are tangents to the circle, centre O. ∠FDE = 50°, ∠DEF = 62° and RO = 2·5 cm. Calculate ∠DOR, ∠ROP, DR and DE.

9. Fig. 84 shows three radii of a circle.

(i) Express the length of arc AB as a fraction of the circumference.

(ii) Find the length of arc BC in terms of π.

(iii) Express the area of sector AOC, where O is the centre of the circle, as a fraction of the area of the circle.

(iv) Find the length of chord AB.

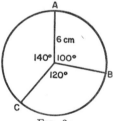

FIG. 84

10. Draw a circle of radius 3·5 cm. Draw radii OP and OQ such that $\angle POQ = 120°$. Construct tangents at P and Q. Let T be their point of intersection and measure PT and QT.

11. Construct Fig. 83 as follows. Draw a circle, centre O, radius 2·5 cm. Draw OP, OQ and OR. Construct the tangents at P, Q and R. Measure DE.

TEST PAPERS

PAPER I

1.   (i) Which of the numbers from 30 to 40 are prime numbers? Find their product.
  (ii) Express 36 in terms of its prime factors.
  (iii) Express 32 as a power of 2.
  (iv) Which denary number is 100100 in binary notation?
  (v) Write 38 in the scale of 6.

2. $3x + 2y = 10$.

  (i) If $x = 6y$, find y.
  (ii) If $x = -4$, find y.
  (iii) What positive whole numbers satisfy the equation?
  (iv) If also $x - 2y = 12$, find x and y.

3. Two pieces of card have lengths of 44 cm and widths of 10 cm. One is bent to form four sides of a rectangular box and the other is bent to form the curved surface of a cylinder.

  (i) Find the radius of the cylinder.
  (ii) Find the volume of the box.
  (iii) Find the volume of the cylinder.

4.   (i) A certain fertilizer consists of three substances in the ratio $1:2:5$ by weight. How many grammes of each are there in 1 kg? If it is applied at 40 g per m², how many 50 kg sacks are needed for a field of 350 ares? [1 a = 100 m²].
  (ii) Christmas cards are bought at 125p per 100 and sold at 2p each. Find the profit per cent on the outlay.

5. In Fig. 85, ABCD is a rectangle. Find (i) EC, (ii) EB, (iii) $\angle$CBE, (iv) the area of $\triangle$ABE, (v) AN.

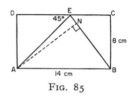

FIG. 85

PAPER 2

1. (i) Express $\frac{7}{16}$ and $\frac{19}{250}$ as exact decimals.

(ii) If 1 international nautical mile $= 1\,852$ metres, express 34 nautical miles in kilometres, correct to the nearest unit.

(iii) Without using tables, find the value of $13\cdot58^2 - 6\cdot42^2$.

(iv) Place in order of size $\frac{1}{6}$, $\frac{3}{20}$, 17%, $(\frac{2}{5})^2$.

2. In $\triangle$ABC, AB = AC = $(3x + 2)$ cm, BC = $4(x - 1)$ cm and altitude AD = $3x$ cm. Express in terms of x:

(i) The perimeter of $\triangle$ABC.

(ii) The area of $\triangle$ABC.

(iii) Cos $\angle$ABC.

(iv) Use Pythagoras' Theorem to find x.

(v) Calculate $\angle$ABC.

3. (i) Express $\dfrac{a}{b} + \dfrac{5b}{3c}$ as a single fraction.

(ii) Express $\dfrac{15x + 8y}{10z}$ as two fractions.

(iii) If $y = px^2 + q$, express x in terms of y, p and q.

(iv) Solve $\dfrac{x - 4}{3} = \dfrac{x}{5}$.

(v) Solve $3x - 4y = 22$, $5x + 6y = 5$.

4. (i) [Fig. 86.) Find $\angle$APB, $\angle$BAP and $\angle$PDC. Name two congruent triangles. Name two similar triangles.

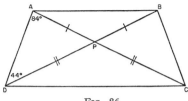

FIG. 86

(ii) A cube of edge 6 cm is painted red and then cut into cubes of edge 2 cm. How many have three red faces, how many have two, how many have one and how many have none?

5. During one week a shopkeeper sold 100 articles at a profit of $33\frac{1}{3}\%$ of the cost price which was £1·80 per dozen. The next week he sold 120 at a discount of 5% of the previous selling price. Find his actual profit in each of the two weeks.

PAPER 3

1. $y = (5 + x)(x - 2)(x - 6).$
  (i) Find y when $x = 0$.
  (ii) Find y when $x = 5$.
  (iii) State three values of x for which $y = 0$.
  (iv) What can you say about y when $2 < x < 6$?

2. ABCD is a rectangle and BE is an arc of a circle, centre A.
  Write down expressions for:

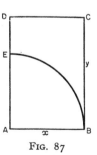

  (i) the area of quadrant AEB,
  (ii) the area of BCDE,
  (iii) the length of arc BE.

If $x = 2·8$ cm and $y = 4·5$ cm, find the perimeter of BCDE.

If $x = 7$ cm, find the value of y so that arc BE divides the rectangle into two equal areas.

FIG. 87

3. (i) Simplify $(4\frac{1}{4} - 3\frac{1}{8}) \div (3\frac{1}{4} + 4\frac{1}{3})$.

(ii) Find the largest denary number which has eight digits when expressed as a binary number.

(iii) Use tables to find $\sqrt{697}$, $\dfrac{1}{58 \cdot 27}$, $(0 \cdot 784)^3$.

(iv) If sin A = 0·8511, find A, cos A and tan A.

4. (i) On a certain day, 4% of the children at a school were absent. 15% of those present did not have school dinners. If 714 dinners were served, how many children were there on the school registers?

(ii) Three men formed a partnership with sums of money in the ratio 3 : 2 : 5. The total sum was £6 000. How much did each contribute? When the profits were shared out, the first man got £405. How much did the others get?

5. Without using a protractor, construct △PQR having QR = 7·8 cm, ∠Q = 60° and ∠R = 45°. Construct a circle of radius 5 cm to pass through Q and R. Construct also a circle to touch the three sides of the triangle. Measure the distance between the two centres.

PAPER 4

1. $a = x(x - 2)$; $b = x(x + 2)$; $c = x^2 - 4$.

Express in terms of x (i) $b - a$, (ii) ba, (iii) $\dfrac{1}{a} + \dfrac{1}{b}$, (iv) $\dfrac{ab}{c}$,

giving each answer in its simplest form.

For what values of x is $b = 0$?

For what values of x is $c = 0$?

For what values of x is a negative?

Sketch the graphs of the three functions.

2. A car does a journey of 150 km at 60 km/h and returns the same distance at 90 km/h. Find (i) the time for the double journey and (ii) the average speed.

If the car uses 27 litres of petrol costing 7½p per litre, find

(iii) the total cost of the petrol and

(iv) the average rate of petrol consumption in cubic centimetres per kilometre.

3. In Fig. 88, O is the centre of the circle and the radius is 5 cm.

(i) Find angles BOP, OBP, APB and AQP.

(ii) Calculate AP and PB.

(iii) Calculate the area of △APB and the length of altitude PN.

FIG. 88

4. A man invests £500 in Extown Building Society which pays 4% p.a. interest and £500 in Wyeshire County Council Bonds which pay him 6½% p.a. interest. On the interest from the bonds he must pay 40% income tax, but the Building Society interest is free of tax. Which is the better investment and by how much?

5. Rain falling on a flat rectangular roof 7·5 m by 5·5 m flows into a cylindrical tank of radius 0·5 m. Find, in centimetres, the increase in the depth of water in the tank caused by 4 mm of rain.

If the cylinder has a height of 1·8 m, find its capacity in litres, correct to the nearest ten litres.

PAPER 5

1. $a = 2x + 3; b = x - 2$

(i) Express in terms of x: $2a + 3b$, ab and $\dfrac{a^2 - b^2}{a + b}$.

(ii) Express x in terms of a.

(iii) Express a in terms of b.

(iv) Find x so that $2a + b = 0$.

2. (i) Find the Simple Interest on £480 for 5 yrs. at 4½% p.a.

(ii) Use logarithms to calculate $\sqrt[3]{0·0725}$ and $42·63 \div 0·237$.

(iii) Solve $2x^2 + x = 28$.

(iv) The interior angle of a regular polygon is 144°. How many sides has the polygon? If A, B, C and D are consecutive vertices, calculate ∠ABD.

3. Fig. 89 shows a wedge (triangular prism). Find (i) the volume of the solid, (ii) the total area of the faces, (iii) the length of EC, and (iv) the size of $\angle$ BCA.

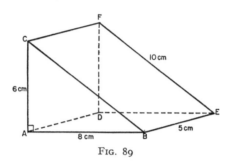

FIG. 89

If the solid is cut into two parts by a cut passing through B, D and F, how many faces will the left hand part have and what will be its volume?

4. A washing machine is priced at £51.

(i) It can be obtained by a deposit of $\frac{1}{6}$ of the price and 24 monthly payments of £1·95. How much more does it cost by this method?

(ii) A retailer allows a discount of 4% to a customer paying cash. How much does the customer pay?

(iii) The retailer allows 20% profit on his cost price when fixing the price of £51. What is his cost price?

5. A boat left A at 10.40 a.m. and travelled at 15 knots in the direction S. 35° E. reaching B at noon. It left B at 1 p.m. and travelled at 12 knots on a course N. 70° E. reaching C at 2.15 p.m.

(i) How far east of A is C?

(ii) How far south of A is C?

(iii) Find the bearing of C from A.

ANSWERS

Exercise 1 (page 3)

1. 6, 4, 3, 4   **2.** 3, 5, 2, 6   **3.** 0, 4, 7, 4

4. 6, 4, 6   **5.** 9, 1, 6   **6.** 3, 2, 6, 2, 2 :17, 112

7. 2516 ÷ 37; 68   **8.** 28   **9.** 41

10. 238

Exercise 2 (page 3)

1. 154; 2,674   **2.** 567; 3,897

3. 42, 63   **4.** 48, 60

5. 101, 103, 107, 109, 113   **6.** 41, 53, 73

7. 9, 49, 121, 144   **8.** 25, 81, 169, 400; 5, 9, 13, 20

9. 8, 27, 64   **10.** 216; 166,375

11. 16; 128; 45; 49,000; 100

12. $2^3 \times 3 \times 5^2$; 7^4; $3^2 \times 5 \times 7^2$

13. 2, 3, 4, 6, 9, 12, 18; 2, 3; 4, 9

14. $2^2 \times 3$; 3×5^2; $2^4 \times 7$; $2^2 \times 5^2$

15. $2^2 \times 3^4$; 18; 26; 34; 55

16. $2^2 \times 7$; 3×7; 84; 72; 100; 160

17. 24, 48, 72, 96; 24   **18.** 90, 180; 90

19. $2^2.3^2$; $2^3.5$; 360   **20.** 28

21. 6; 5; 16; 22; 105   **22.** $2.3^3.5.7$; 42, 45, 54

23. 3, 47; 7, 43; 13, 37; 19, 31

24. Even; odd   **25.** 7^2; $(1 + 2 + ... + 7)^2$; n^2

Exercise 3 (page 5)

1. 111, 1010, 1001, 10011, 101101, 1101010

2. 5, 6, 14, 18, 27, 44   **3.** 1011; 1001; 11101

4. 1011; 1101; 101

5. 110111; 10010110; 10001111

6. 11; 101; 111 **7.** 64 **8.** 17

9. 322 **10.** 12 **11.** 0·5, 0·25, 0·375

12. $\frac{1}{2}, \frac{1}{3}, \frac{1}{6}$ **13.** 13; 7 **14.** 13; 9

15. 12; 14 **16.** 112; 155 **18.** 9; 7

19. 7; 5

Exercise 4 (page 6)

1. 700 **2.** £2·50 **3.** 625

4. 10 h 27 min; 47 min **5.** 125

6. 3·1 kg **7.** 85p **8.** £7·27

9. £21·84 **10.** 21·5 kg; 465 **11.** 48 days

12. £3·18 **13.** £1·35

14. 10.47 a.m., 11.12 p.m.

Exercise 5 (page 8)

1. 40 min **2.** 20 h **3.** 45s **4.** 24s

5. 6, 9 **6.** 3, 6, 21 **7.** 2 **8.** 1

9. 12 **10.** 38 **11.** $\frac{8}{20}, \frac{15}{20}, \frac{14}{20}$

12. $\frac{8}{18}, \frac{9}{18}, \frac{12}{18}, \frac{15}{18}$ **13.** $\frac{13}{20}, \frac{5}{8}, \frac{3}{5}$ **14.** $\frac{5}{12}, \frac{2}{5}, \frac{1}{3}, \frac{4}{15}$

19. $\frac{29}{36}$ **20.** $1\frac{5}{12}$ **21.** $3\frac{13}{24}$ **22.** $\frac{3}{14}$

23. $2\frac{9}{20}$ **24.** $2\frac{15}{16}$ **25.** $\frac{6}{35}$ **26.** $\frac{7}{12}$

27. $1\frac{13}{15}$ **28.** $3\frac{1}{3}$ **29.** 32 **30.** 27

31. $\frac{2}{7}$ **32.** $\frac{2}{5}$ **33.** $\frac{3}{4}$ **34.** $1\frac{2}{3}$

35. $\frac{5}{12}$ **36.** 2 **37.** 1 **38.** 0

39. $\frac{1}{6}$ **40.** $1\frac{3}{16}$ **41.** $2\frac{2}{9}$ **42.** $10\frac{4}{5}$

43. $10\frac{1}{2}$ **44.** $8\frac{3}{4}$ **45.** $\frac{7}{9}$ **46.** $1\frac{1}{9}$

47. 25p **48.** $\frac{19}{24}$ **49.** 35 **50.** 22

51. 60p **52.** 35p **53.** 44p **54.** $62\frac{1}{2}$p

55. 13 min 20 s   **56.** 33 min 45 s   **57.** 45p

58. 212p   **59.** 29p   **60.** 57p

61. $\frac{3}{20}$ **62.** $\frac{1}{32}$ **63.** $\frac{3}{11}$ **64.** $\frac{7}{9}$

EXERCISE 6 (page 9)

1. 2·56   **2.** 10·57   **3.** 2·47   **4.** 5·16

5. 2·68   **6.** 37·2   **7.** 240   **8.** 0·6

9. 0·067   **10.** 0·024   **11.** 0·092   **12.** 1·74

13. 0·06   **14.** 0·56   **15.** 0·022   **16.** 0·16

17. 0·0144   **18.** 138   **19.** 2·96   **20.** 0·3

21. 17·68   **22.** 0·39   **23.** 0·021   **24.** 1·5

25. 3·84, 2·45, 26·57, 0·08   **26.** 5·7, 26·2, 0·1, 18·0

27. 6·5, 360, 0·074, 0·30

28. 0·4   **29.** 0·45   **30.** 0·14   **31.** 0·08

32. $\frac{4}{5}$ **33.** $\frac{3}{50}$ **34.** $\frac{11}{20}$ **35.** $\frac{3}{8}$

36. 0·667   **37.** 0·571   **38.** 0·583   **39.** 0·061

40. 4·56   **41.** 2·52   **42.** 0·1156   **43.** 3·7

44. 0·37   **45.** 3·05   **46.** 18·48   **47.** 0·2̇7̇

48. 0·4̇28571̇   **49.** 0·2̇   **50.** 0·2̇30769̇

51. 0·62; 0·054; 3·28; 0·007   **52.** 0·025; 4·729; 0·003; 0·15

53. 5 800; 0·065; 600; 0·03   **54.** 0·0095   **55.** 0·057

56. 0·41   **57.** 0·4; 0·65   **58.** 42 min; 51 min

59. £0·325, £650   **60.** 0·94p

EXERCISE 7 (page 11)

1. 0·25, 25%; $\frac{2}{5}$, 40%; $\frac{3}{20}$, 0·15; 0·625, 62$\frac{1}{2}$%; 0·3̇, 33$\frac{1}{3}$%; $\frac{3}{100}$, 3%

2. $\frac{17}{20}$, $\frac{9}{25}$, $\frac{3}{8}$, $\frac{1}{40}$, $\frac{19}{80}$

3. 40%, 15%, 66$\frac{2}{3}$%, 47$\frac{1}{5}$%, 42$\frac{6}{7}$%

4. £18; 56%; £70   **5.** 64%; 70p, £56

6. £12; £12·50; £10·70   **7.** £9; £8; £6

8. £18, 75%   **9.** 93 fr., 18 fr.   **10.** $60, $21

11. £224, £28   **12.** 5%   **13.** £154

14. £6·25   **15.** 65%, 68%; 3%   **16.** £2·27½

17. 60   **18.** £101·25   **19.** £900

20. 25%

EXERCISE 8 (page 12)

1. 21   **2.** 88 km   **3.** 58⅔   **4.** 79

5. 69·8 kg   **6.** 16 yr 8 m   **7.** 997·3 mb

8. $\frac{1}{3}(a + b + c)$; $(xp + yt)/(x + y)$ g   **9.** 18 kg

10. 63%

EXERCISE 9 (page 13)

1. 72 km/h   **2.** 3h 48 min   **3.** 833 m

4. 126 km/h

5. 25 m/s; 15 m/s   **6.** 27 km/h

7. 70 km/h   **8.** 5   **9.** 138

10. 36 min, 9·6 km, 11·4 km   **11.** 48 km/h

12. 78 km/h   **13.** 30 min, 20 min, 19·2 km/h

EXERCISE 10 (page 14)

1. £1·50, £2·50, £3   **2.** 10·5 cm

3. £279   **4.** £1·25, 80p   **5.** 9:16

6. 100 g   **7.** 40, 30, 12 fr   **8.** £37·50

9. 480 m, 14·4 ha   **10.** 20 cm

11. 1 204 m²

EXERCISE 11 (page 15)

1. 650 m   **2.** 80 cm   **3.** 230 km

4. 9 min   **5.** 11 400   **6.** 27 rev/s

7. 14 days   **8.** 801 sch   **9.** 360

10. 8 h 20 min   **11.** £1·55

EXERCISE 12 (page 16)

1. £30   **2.** £16·80   **3.** 546 fr   **4.** $162.90

5. 5%   **6.** 5 years   **7.** 2 250 fr   **8.** 20 yr

9. £340   **10.** 1 025 fr   **11.** £40·80   **12.** 43 fr 26 c

13. £1·87½   **14.** £405, £364·50

15. £34 300   **16.** £131·08

EXERCISE 13 (page 17)

1. 1,910; 14,880; 0·1910; 0·01488

2. 1·918; 19·18; 0·1918; 0·06066

3. 0·2349; 0·02349; 2·349; 23·49

4. 0·3077   **5.** 0·244   **6.** 386·5   **7.** 6·022

8. 0·8897   **9.** 0·6385   **10.** 0·8542, 2·8542, $\bar{2}$·8542

11. 2·379, 23·79, 0·002379   **12.** $\bar{4}$·2, 0·2, 4·5, $\bar{4}$·5

13. $\bar{4}$·4, 4·4, $\bar{6}$·4, 3·6   **14.** 8·4, $\bar{4}$·4, $\bar{3}$·0, $\bar{9}$·6

15. 1·8, $\bar{2}$·8, $\bar{1}$·52, $\bar{2}$·8   **16.** 153·3   **17.** 6·902

18. 2,048   **19.** 7·731   **20.** 14·19   **21.** 97·88

22. 2·473   **23.** 3·052   **24.** 60·22   **25.** 0·8235

26. 0·06966   **27.** 4·840   **28.** 0·5616   **29.** 0·9380

30. 74·49   **31.** 56·99   **32.** 5·794   **33.** 0·7047

34. 39·6   **35.** 4·13   **36.** 239   **37.** 3·53

38. 387,100,000; 0·3871   **39.** 3,327   **40.** 16, 11

41. log 18, log 6, log 8, log 3, log 500

42. 0·69897, 0·90309, $\bar{1}$·69897

43. $a + b$, $a - b$, $2a$, $\frac{1}{2}b$, $5b$, $2 + a$, $-2 + b$

44. $x + y$, $3x$, $-y$, $\frac{1}{2}x$

EXERCISE 14 (page 19)

1. 413·70 fr   **2.** 9 698 l   **3.** 208·12 m

4. 42p   **5.** £112·20   **6.** £4·09

7. £5·19   **8.** £16·50

EXERCISE 15 (page 20)

1. Constant speed of 60 km/h; 30 km/h; 2 km; 2 min and 20 min; 18 km; 45 km/h

2. 187, 91·80, 217·60, 1 260 kr; £5·88, £9·41, £13·29, £47·10

3. 37 yr, £209   **4.** 114 mm, 14

5. 2·06 days, 4·12 days   **6.** £2·50, £3·70; 160

7. 11.50 a.m., 6 km/h; 12.7 p.m.

EXERCISE 16 (page 22)

1. 3·6 ha   **2.** 186 g   **3.** 266   **4.** 19

5. 3; 6, 10, 12 cm²; Yes, $12\frac{1}{4}$ cm²; Yes

6. 27 cm³   **7.** 4·8 m³; 75 cm

8. 50·4 cm   **9.** 84 cm²

10. 96 cm², 9·6 cm   **11.** 60 cm²

12. 1 960 m²   **13.** 20 cm

14. 27 cm³, 66 cm²   **15.** 96 cm³

16. 61·3 cm²   **17.** 3 000 m³; 41 h 40 min

18. 7·6 m³; 15·58 m²; 5 m²

19. 21 cm²   **20.** 48 cm³; 104 cm²

EXERCISE 17 (page 25)

1. 176 cm, 2 500   **2.** 220 mm, 33 m

3. 302 m   **4.** 346·5 cm²   **5.** 12·1 m²

6. 51 cm²   **7.** 154 cm²   **8.** 252 cm²

9. 264 cm²   **10.** 42·6 1   **11.** 56

12. 172 cm², 279 cm³   **13.** $513\frac{1}{3}$ cm³

14. $179\frac{2}{3}$ cm³, 154 cm²   **15.** $\frac{31}{42}$, 211 g

16. 6 286 cm³   **17.** 96 m³   **18.** 4·5 m

19. 9 cm   **20.** $18\frac{1}{2}$ cm   **21.** $\frac{1}{2}$, $\frac{1}{3}$; $\frac{1}{3}$, $\frac{1}{7}$

EXERCISE 18 (page 27)

1. £2·03   **2.** £1 040; £338·40

3. £4·80; £5·18   **4.** £1·90

5. £4; £73·33   **6.** £5 200; £1 760; £220

7. $106\frac{1}{4}$p in £; £27 600; £552·50

8. £6 290; £629 000; £84·64

9. £86·25; £2·55; £662

EXERCISE 19 (page 29)

1. 1, 4, 2, 5, −8, 0, 2   **2.** 0, −1, 3, 7

3. 9, 1, $2\frac{1}{4}$, −4   **4.** $-1\frac{1}{2}$, −9, 9, 8

5. 8, −7   **6.** 0, 3, −2   **7.** −3, 18, $-5\frac{1}{3}$

8. −2, 1, 0   **9.** First, 8   **10.** 6   **11.** 23, $4\frac{1}{4}$

12. 15   **13.** −20   **14.** 26   **15.** 20

16. 40   **17.** 1, $\frac{5}{9}$ **18.** 4, −15

EXERCISE 20 (page 30)

1. $16a$ **2.** $-3b$ **3.** $15c$ **4.** $14d$

5. $3e + 5f$ **6.** $2g + 7h$ **7.** $8k - 7m$ **8.** $6p - n$

9. a^3 **10.** b^5 **11.** $6a^2$ **12.** $8b^2$

13. $25c^2$ **14.** $6ab$ **15.** a^5 **16.** b^4

17. $6a^5$ **18.** $20a^2b$ **19.** a^6 **20.** b^{15}

21. $9c^6$ **22.** $\frac{1}{8}d^6$ **23.** a^5 **24.** b^5

25. 7   **26.** $\frac{2}{3}$ **27.** $4a^2$ **28.** $5ab^2$

29. $3a - 6b + 3c$ **30.** $d^2 - 2de + df$

31. $-g^2 + 5g$ **32.** $6hj - 15h^2$

33. $k^3 + 3k^2$ **34.** $-14m^2 + 8m^3$

35. $3p - 2\frac{1}{2}$ **36.** $2 - \frac{1}{5}t^2$ **37.** $10 - 6v$ **38.** $9x + 12y$

39. a^3 **40.** a^2 **41.** $10a^4b$ **42.** $2c^5$

EXERCISE 21 (page 31)

1. $ac + ad + bc + bd$ **2.** $p^2 - pq - pr + qr$

3. $cd + 4c - 3d - 12$ **4.** $12 + 2f - 6g - fg$

5. $x^2 + 5x + 6$ **6.** $y^2 + 10y + 24$

7. $a^2 - 6a + 5$ **8.** $b^2 - 9b + 18$

9. $c^2 + 5c - 24$ **10.** $d^2 - 5d - 14$

11. $2x^2 + 13x + 15$ **12.** $3y^2 - 11y + 10$

13. $15x^2 + x - 2$ **14.** $8 + 2y - 3y^2$

15. $6a^2 + 5a - 6$ **16.** $10b^2 - 7b - 12$

17. $2x^4 + 15x^2 + 18$ **18.** $28 + 17c - 3c^2$

19. $x^2 + 8x + 16$ **20.** $y^2 - 6y + 9$

21. $9a^2 - 6a + 1$ **22.** $25b^2 + 10b + 1$

23. $2x^2 + 2y^2$ **24.** $2a^2 - 2ab$

25. $4a^2 + 12a + 9$ **26.** $9b^2 - 30b + 25$

27. $x^2 - 49$ **28.** $y^2 - 25$

29. $16x^2 + 24xy + 9y^2$ **30.** $9 - p^2$

31. a^2 **32.** $p^2 + q^2$ **33.** $-2xy$ **34.** $24xy$

37. $x + 3, 3x + 4$

EXERCISE 22 (page 32)

1. $x(x + 5)$ **2.** $a(b - 1)$ **3.** $3c(c - 2)$

4. $5d^2(3 + 4d)$ **5.** $3x^2y^2(2y - 3x)$ **6.** $\pi r(r + 2h)$

7. $3bc(3a - 2d)$ **8.** $5x^3y^2(y^2 - 2xy + 3x^2)$

9. $4m^2p(2m^2p - 3q^3)$ **10.** $9kn^2(2k^2 - 3kn - n^2)$

11. $(a + 3)(a - 3)$ **12.** $(5 + b)(5 - b)$ **13.** $(2c + 1)(2c - 1)$

14. $(3d + 4)(3d - 4)$ **15.** $(pq + 1)(pq - 1)$

16. $(6x + 7)(6x - 7)$ **17.** $a(a + 3)(a - 3)$

18. $b(b + 1)(b - 1)$ **19.** $3(c + 5)(c - 5)$

20. $a(a - b)$; 9,480 **21.** $(x + y)(x - y)$; 1,200

22. 759 **23.** 1,000 **24.** 140 **25.** 3,060

26. 330 **27.** $(a + 3)(a + 2)$ **28.** $(b + 5)(b + 2)$

29. $(c - 5)(c - 1)$ **30.** $(d - 4)(d - 2)$ **31.** $(a + 6)(a - 1)$

32. $(b + 5)(b - 2)$ **33.** $(c - 5)(c + 1)$ **34.** $(d - 4)(d + 2)$

35. $(e + 4)(e - 3)$ **36.** $(1 + 6a)(1 + a)$

37. $(1 - 2b)(1 + b)$ **38.** $(10 - c)(1 - c)$

39. $a(b - 3)(b - 1)$ **40.** $2(c + 3)(c + 1)$

41. $3(d - 3)(d + 2)$ **42.** $(2a + 3)(a + 1)$

43. $(3b - 2)(b - 1)$ **44.** $(3c + 1)(c - 2)$

45. $(5d - 3)(d + 1)$ **46.** $(2e - 5)(e + 2)$

47. $2(2f + 3)(3f - 1)$

48. $(a - 3)(a + 1)$; $(b + 3)(b - 1)$; $(c - 3)(c - 1)$

49. $(x + 3)(x + 7)$; 13×17

50. $(2x + 3)(2x + 1)$; $3 \times 7 \times 23$

51. $(x - y)(b + c)$ **52.** $(3p + 2)(2u - 5)$

53. $(b + d)(a - c)$ **54.** $(h + 2)(f + 5)$ **55.** $(m - 3)(m + p)$

56. $(x - y)(y - 4)$ **57.** $(a + 3)(b - 5)$ **58.** $(3c - d)(1 - 2d)$

59. $(3a - 2)(p - 3)$ **60.** $(x + y)(x + 7)$

61. $(x + y)(1 + a)$ **62.** $(3p - 1)(p - 2q)$

63. $(1 - 2x)(1 + 2y)(1 - 2y)$ **64.** $(a + b)(1 + a - b)$

65. $p(4 - p)(3 + q)$ **66.** $2(f + 2)(g - 5)$

67. $(a + 5)^2$ **68.** $(b - 7)^2$ **69.** $(c + 6)^2$

70. $(d + \frac{1}{3})^2$ **71.** $(e - \frac{1}{2})^2$ **72.** $(1 + 3f)^2$

73. $(2x + 1)^2$ **74.** $(3y - 1)^2$ **75.** $(2z - 3)^2$

76. $a(b+4)^2$ **77.** $3(2p-1)^2$ **78.** $(x^2-8)^2$

79. 81 **80.** 121 **81.** 1

82. $100; x+10$ **83.** $\frac{1}{25}; x+\frac{1}{5}$ **84.** $\frac{1}{16}; x-\frac{1}{4}$

85. $9; (2x-3)$

EXERCISE 23 (page 34)

1. $\frac{b}{c}; 2d; \frac{2e^2}{3}; -\frac{3f}{h}$ **2.** $p^2r; \frac{t^4}{2}; -4y; \frac{ac}{5b^2}$

3. $ab; ab; 3b; -2b$ **4.** $cd^2; 3cd; 3e; cd(c+d)$

5. $c(a-b); ac; c(a+b)$ **6.** $\frac{a}{12}$

7. $\frac{5}{6b}$ **8.** $\frac{3d+2c}{cd}$ **9.** $\frac{1}{2g}$

10. $\frac{9-2h}{6}$ **11.** $\frac{m-p}{mp}$ **12.** $\frac{t^2+q^2}{qt}$

13. $\frac{2z-5x-3y}{6xyz}$ **14.** $\frac{3b^2+2ab-a^2}{a^2b^2}$ **15.** $\frac{d}{c(c-d)}$

16. $\frac{a-b}{2}$ **17.** 3 **18.** $\frac{c-d}{c}$ **19.** $\frac{g}{f+g}$

20. $\frac{5}{h+1}$ **21.** $\frac{k+1}{k}$ **22.** $\frac{5-a}{3}$ **23.** $\frac{c+2}{6}$

24. $\frac{ab}{6}$ **25.** $2d$ **26.** $\frac{a+3}{a-2}$ **27.** $b-c$

28. $\frac{x}{x+2y}; \frac{x-2y}{x-y}; x(x-y)$

EXERCISE 24 (page 35)

1. 7 **2.** 11 **3.** $4\frac{1}{2}$ **4.** 18 **5.** 4

6. 6 **7.** -1 **8.** -3 **9.** $2\frac{3}{4}$ **10.** -12

11. 12 **12.** $10\frac{2}{3}$ **13.** 7 **14.** 8 **15.** 17

16. 5   **17.** −2   **18.** 4   **19.** 2   **20.** $\frac{1}{5}$

21. $4\frac{1}{2}$ **22.** 7   **23.** −1·2   **24.** 5   **25.** 4

26. 1, 4; 2, 3; 3, 2; 4, 1   **27.** 1, 7; 4, 5; 7, 3; 10, 1

28. $7\frac{1}{2}$ **29.** 7   **30.** 5   **31.** 2   **32.** −3

33. −$\frac{1}{2}$ **34.** $\frac{1}{6}$ **35.** 4

36. 8, 9, 10   **37.** 6; 25   **38.** 8

39. $3x$; $5(17 - x)$; 8   **40.** 120

41. 20; isosceles   **42.** 0·8 km

EXERCISE 25 (page 37)

1. 2, 1   **2.** −1, 3   **3.** 5, −2   **4.** 2, 5

5. 3, 4   **6.** 3, −2   **7.** −1, 2   **8.** $\frac{1}{2}$, −$1\frac{1}{2}$

9. $\frac{3}{4}$, −$\frac{2}{3}$ **10.** $\frac{1}{3}$, $\frac{2}{3}$ **11.** 6, 5   **12.** 3, −5

13. 5   **14.** 1   **15.** −3, −2   **16.** $\frac{1}{2}$, −$1\frac{1}{2}$

17. 4p   **18.** 34, 15   **19.** 13, 17   **20.** 8p

21. 7, $5\frac{1}{2}$

EXERCISE 26 (page 38)

1. 6, 2, 0, 0, 6, 20   **2.** 10, 4, 0, −2, −2, 0

3. 0, −3, −4, 0   **4.** 5, −7   **5.** −$\frac{1}{3}$, $4\frac{1}{2}$

6. 5, −7   **7.** −3, −1   **8.** −$\frac{1}{2}$, $1\frac{2}{3}$ **9.** 0, 10

10. 4, 5   **11.** −2, −3   **12.** 2, −1   **13.** −7, 2

14. 0, 3   **15.** 3, −3   **16.** $\frac{1}{2}$, $\frac{1}{3}$ **17.** −$1\frac{1}{2}$, 1

18. 1, $\frac{2}{3}$ **19.** 0, −$\frac{4}{5}$ **20.** ±$2\frac{1}{2}$ **21.** −$\frac{1}{2}$, −$1\frac{1}{2}$

22. −$\frac{2}{5}$, 1   **23.** $\frac{1}{7}$, 1   **24.** $\frac{1}{2}$, −2   **25.** $\frac{1}{4}$, −3

26. −$2\frac{1}{2}$, 0   **27.** −$1\frac{1}{2}$, $2\frac{1}{2}$ **28.** ±2·65   **29.** ±1·66

30. ±0·82   **31.** ±3·16   **32.** 3·45, −1·45

33. 7·47, −1·47   **34.** −0·20, −9·80   **35.** 7·74, 0·26

36. 2·62, 0·38   **37.** 1·22, −8·22   **38.** 1·21, −3·71

39. −3·13, −0·53   **40.** 2·34, −0·34   **41.** −0·84, 0·59

42. 4   **43.** 5, 8 (or −5, −8)   **44.** 8 cm

EXERCISE 27 (page 39)

1. $(x - n)$ yr   **2.** $60y$ **3.** $2nx$ pence

4. xt km, $\dfrac{n}{x}$ h   **5.** $\dfrac{60n}{t}$

6. $(xy + wz)$ pence   **7.** $2(xy + yz + zx)$ cm²

8. $(x - y - 10)$ pence   **9.** $\dfrac{xw}{1\,000}$ kg

10. $\dfrac{ax + by}{x + y}$ m/s   **11.** $\pounds\dfrac{xnt}{100}$

12. $2ac + 2bc + 4c^2$ m²

EXERCISE 28 (page 40)

1. 154   **2.** $112\frac{1}{2}$ **3.** 88   **4.** 264

5. 0·75   **6.** $\frac{4}{5}$ **7.** 11   **8.** $2\frac{1}{4}$

9. 666   **10.** 15   **11.** 12

12. $\pi(a^2 - b^2)l$; 99   **13.** 25, 40, 40, −80; 45 m

EXERCISE 29 (page 41)

1. $b - a$ **2.** $c + d$ **3.** f/e **4.** gh

5. $\dfrac{n - m}{k}$ **6.** $\sqrt{p}$ **7.** $\dfrac{1}{r}$ **8.** $\dfrac{su}{t}$

9. $\dfrac{A}{b}$ **10.** $\dfrac{c}{\pi}$

11. $\frac{1}{2}p - b$ **12.** $180 - A - C$

13. bt **14.** $\dfrac{p}{s}$ **15.** $\sqrt{\dfrac{A}{\pi}}$ **16.** $\sqrt[3]{V}$

17. $\dfrac{v - u}{t}$ **18.** $\dfrac{v^2 - u^2}{2f}$ **19.** $\dfrac{2s}{t^2}$ **20.** $\sqrt{\left(\dfrac{4wl}{3b}\right)}$

21. $\sqrt{\left(\dfrac{V}{\pi h}\right)}$ **22.** $\sqrt[3]{\left(\dfrac{3V}{4\pi}\right)}$ **23.** $\dfrac{2A}{a + b}$ **24.** $\dfrac{uf}{u - f}$

25. $\dfrac{2A}{h} - b$ **26.** $p = 4x,\ n = x^2,\ n = \dfrac{p^2}{16}$

Exercise 30 (page 42)

1. A, $y = \dfrac{4}{x}$: B, $y = 4x - x^2$: C, $y = 4$: D, $y = 4 - \tfrac{1}{2}x$:

E, $y = x^2 - 8x + 16$ **2.** $5,\ -4$

3. 6; 3 and -2; 3; -2 **4.** $31\frac{1}{4}$ m; $3\cdot6$ s

5. $3\frac{1}{4}$ h, $26\frac{2}{3}$ km/h **6.** $-0\cdot6,\ 1\cdot4$; $2\cdot5$

7. B; $0\cdot72$; $(3, 4\frac{1}{2})$ and $(-1, \frac{1}{2})$; $2x,\ 3$

8. $1\cdot30,\ -2\cdot30$; $2\cdot71,\ -2\cdot21$; $3\cdot24,\ 1\cdot73$

9. $2\cdot6 < x < 4\cdot8$

10. 4; $3\cdot36$; $0\cdot59 < x < 3\cdot41$; $0\cdot59, 3\cdot41$; No solution exists for the first equation. The second equation has two solutions which could be found by extending the graph.

Exercise 31 (page 45)

1. $x > 3$ **2.** $x > 4\frac{1}{2}$ **3.** $x < 5\frac{2}{3}$

4. $x < -3$ **5.** $x > -1\frac{1}{2}$ **6.** $x < -6$

7. $11 \geqslant x \geqslant 4$ **8.** $x \geqslant 5$ **9.** $x \leqslant -3$

10. $x \geqslant 33$ **11.** $8 \geqslant x \geqslant 5$ **12.** $-1 \geqslant x \geqslant -5$

13. $+, -$ **14.** $-, +$ **15.** $+, +, -$

16. $+, +, -$ **17.** $+, +, -$ **18.** $-, -, +$

19. $4 > x > -1$ **20.** $x > \frac{1}{2},\ x < -\frac{1}{3}$ **21.** $5 > y > -11$

22. $-1 > m > -3\frac{1}{2}$ **23.** (i) $<$, (iii) $<$, (iv) $>$

24. $5 > x > -3$ **25.** $2, 5$ **26.** $3, 6$

27. $5, 3$ **28.** 5 **29.** 4

30. $(1, 1), (1, 2), (2, 1), (3, 1)$ **31.** $(2, 1), (3, 2), (3, 3), (4, 4)$

34. 5

EXERCISE 32 (page 46)

1. a^7 **2.** a^3 **3.** a^{10} **4.** b^9

5. c^6 **6.** d^6 **7.** e^5 **8.** f^7

9. g^6 **10.** h^4 **11.** j^5 **12.** k^4

13. m^8 **14.** p^9 **15.** $\dfrac{1}{t^3}$ **16.** $\dfrac{1}{x^2}$

17. 27   **18.** 16   **19.** 1,000   **20.** 125

21. 49   **22.** 8   **23.** a^{4x} **24.** b^{6y}

25. c^{3z} **26.** $\dfrac{1}{d^{2x}}$ **27.** $\dfrac{1}{f^x}$ **28.** g^{2y+x}

29. 6; 5   **30.** $2^2 \times 3^4$; 324

31. $2^6 \times 3^3$; 1,728   **32.** $2^8 \times 5^4$; 160,000

33. $2^2 \times 3$; 12   **34.** 100   **35.** 0·01   **36.** 10,000

37. 0·001   **38.** 10^5 **39.** 10^{-1} **40.** 10^6

41. 10^{-5} **42.** 470   **43.** 58,000   **44.** 6,000

45. 342·9   **46.** 0·032   **47.** 0·00087   **48.** 0·005

49. 0·4012   **50.** $2·94 \times 10^2$

51. $7·532 \times 10^4$ **52.** $2·304 \times 10^2$

53. $3·642 \times 10$ **54.** $5·6 \times 10^{-2}$ **55.** 7×10^{-4}

56. $5·03 \times 10^{-3}$ **57.** $9·63 \times 10^{-1}$ **58.** $2·3 \times 10^{13}$

59. $1·6 \times 10^{-2}$ **60.** $2·29 \times 10^8$ **61.** 5×10^6

62. $3·65 \times 10^8$ **63.** $1·08 \times 10^9$

EXERCISE 33 (page 48)

1. WSW., NNE., ENE.; $22\frac{1}{2}°$, $247\frac{1}{2}°$, $135°$, $225°$

2. $135°$; $157\frac{1}{2}°$; $75°$; $144°$

3. W. ; S. $60°$ W.; S. $30°$ E., S. $40°$ W.

4. $90°$; $120°$ **5.** $210°$; $15°$ **6.** $15°$; $80°$

7. $80°$; $35°$; $72°$ **8.** $115°$; $20°$; $108°$

9. POR is a straight line; POR and QOS are straight lines

10. *a*, *c*; *a*, *d*; *c*, *d*; 65°   **11.** 50°, 130°, 35°, 15°

12. 75°, 55°, 50°, 75°, 50°   **13.** 68°, 68°, 50°, 62°

14. 116°, 44°   **16.** 13°, 26°

EXERCISE 34 (page 50)

1. 38°; 27°   **2.** No; No; Yes; No   **3.** 50°

4. 90°   **5.** 76°   **6.** 60°   **7.** 55°

8. 70°   **9.** 45°; 30°; 18°

10. 144°; 140°; $157\frac{1}{2}$°   **11.** Yes, 9; No; Yes, 15

12. No; Yes, 18; No   **13.** 38°   **14.** 20

15. 24   **16.** 68°   **17.** 20°   **18.** 60°

19. 30°   **20.** 64°, 58°   **21.** 32°, 25°   **22.** 40°

23. 22°, 123°, 35°   **24.** 45°, 15°, 75°

25. 72°, 72°, 36°; 72°   **26.** 75°, 150°

EXERCISE 35 (page 53)

2. (i) A, B, C, D; (ii) B, D; (iii) E

3. A, B, C, D; (ii) F; (iii) C, D

4. (i) C, D, E; (ii) B, D, F; (iii) E, F; (iv) B, D

6. (i) rect.; (ii) isos. trap.; (iii) par.; (iv) kite

7. (i) rect.; (ii) rhom.; (iii) square

8. $22\frac{1}{2}$°, $112\frac{1}{2}$°, 45°   **9.** 56°   **10.** 90°, 105°

EXERCISE 36 (page 55)

1. 6·94 cm   **2.** 5·51 cm

3. 6·30 cm, 7·56 cm, 7·09 cm   **4.** 3·78 cm

5. 3·78 cm   **8.** 5·6 cm   **11.** 3·06 cm   **12.** 5·2 cm

EXERCISE 37 (page 56)

1. $13\frac{1}{2}$, 12   **2.** 24, 22·4   **3.** 10, 9, 5

4. BCP, DEP; 6, 3·6   **5.** 13·5 m

6. 1·8 m   **7.** 6, $4\frac{1}{2}$, $7\frac{1}{2}$

8. BCE, AHE, ACD; $4\frac{1}{2}$, $1\frac{2}{3}$ **9.** 8, 11; $4\frac{1}{2}$

10. 81 g   **11.** 8 cm²

12. Mult. by 4; mult. by 8; div. by 4

13. 810 cm³   **14.** 6·4 cm², 40 cm²

15. DEF, HJK; $\dfrac{DE}{KJ} = \dfrac{EF}{JH} = \dfrac{FD}{HK}$

16. AB, AQ, BC; 7·2 cm   **17.** 6 cm; 9; 16; 775 cm³

EXERCISE 38 (page 59)

1. $\angle F = 65°$, EF = 6 cm, $\angle C = \angle E = \angle J = 40°$, $\angle K = 75°$

2. LMN and YXZ   **3.** DEF and YZX

4. AB = QR, AC = RP   **5.** $\angle D = \angle Y$, $\angle E = \angle X$

6. IV, II   **7.** ABD, BCE

EXERCISE 39 (page 61)

1. 16 letters; H, I, O, X   **2.** H, I, N, O, S, X, Z

5. 60°, 180°, 120°, 72°, 90°; C

6. 1, 1, infinite, 1, 13, 7

EXERCISE 40 (page 61)

1. 8·4 km   **2.** 7·17 knots   **3.** 179 km, N. 32° W.

4. 66 m, 31 m   **5.** 9·85 knots, $275\frac{1}{2}°$

6. S. $47\frac{1}{2}°$ E., $20\frac{1}{4}$ naut. ml.   **7.** 45 m

EXERCISE 41 (page 62)

1. 10   **2.** 25   **3.** 12   **4.** 15

5. obtuse   **6.** acute   **7.** 90°   **8.** I, II

9. 24 cm   **10.** 6 m   **11.** 17   **12.** 7

13. 8   **14.** 5   **15.** 16   **16.** 8·6

17. 7·5   **18.** 7·1 cm   **19.** 66 m   **20.** 70 cm

21. 130·4 m   **22.** 2, 3   **23.** 5, 7

Exercise 42 (page 64)

1. 4·69 cm   **2.** 32° 0′   **3.** 8·83 cm   **4.** 3·76 cm

5. 36° 52′   **6.** 38° 56′   **7.** 181 m   **8.** 32 m

9. S. 33° 41′ E.   **10.** 73° 44′   **11.** 8·4 m

12. 5·7 m   **13.** 13 cm, 2·4, $\frac{5}{13}$

14. $\frac{4}{5}, \frac{4}{3}$ **15.** 38° 32′ or 33′

16. 5·63 cm.   **17.** 102° 41′

18. 70° 32′, 46 cm   **19.** 1·36 m

20. $\dfrac{PN}{ON}, \dfrac{QA}{OA}; \dfrac{PN}{OP}, \dfrac{QA}{OQ}$; 0·625, 0·530

21. 5·40 cm, 8·09 cm, 27·0 cm²

22. 72°, 8·09 cm, 11·8 cm, 238 cm²

23. 375 m, 253 m, 628 m

24. 157 m

25. 16·1 m, 14·1 m, 8·8 m, 12° 21′

Exercise 43 (page 67)

3. cylinder; cone; sphere   **4.** 5·74 cm   **5.** 6·1 cm

6. 246 m, 65 m   **7.** 4·36 cm   **8.** 2·24 cm

Exercise 44 (page 68)

1. 90°, 90°, 90°; 25°, 25°

2. y; z; $x + w = 180°$; 115°, 230°

3. 55°, 42°, 97°   **4.** 110°

5. 48°   **6.** 70°

8. $p = 60°, t = w = 50°, z = 130°$

9. 100°; parallel   **10.** 104°, 76°

11. 35°, 110°, 70°, 85°, 60°, 110°, 10°

12. 48°, 12°, 60°   **13.** 28°, 90°, 62°, 118°, 34°

14. 56°, 56°, 124°, 62°

15. 30°, 75°, 15°, 105°, 45°, 135°

16. g; h; 75°, 105°, 55°

17. 75°, 42°, 150°   **18.** 76°, 56°, 48°

Exercise 45 (page 71)

1. 10 cm, 73° 44′   **2.** 16 cm, 61° 56′   **3.** 1 cm, 7 cm

4. 6·5 cm   **5.** 12 cm   **6.** 4·47 cm, 48° 11′

7. 112°, 56°, 9·95 cm

8. 65°, 118°, 5·36 cm, 9·52 cm

9. $\frac{5}{18}$; 4π cm; $\frac{7}{18}$; 9·19 cm

10. 6·06 cm   **11.** 9·52 cm

Test Paper 1 (page 73)

1. 31, 37, 1 147; $2^2 \times 3^2$; 2^5; 36; 102

2. $\frac{1}{2}$; 11; 2, 2; $5\frac{1}{2}$, $-3\frac{1}{4}$

3. 7 cm; 1 210 cm³; 1 540 cm³

4. 125 g, 250 g, 625 g; 28; 60%

5. 6 cm; 10 cm; 36° 52′; 56 cm²; 11·2 cm

Test Paper 2 (page 74)

1. 0·4375, 0·076; 63 km; 143·2; $\frac{3}{20}$, $(\frac{2}{5})^2$, $\frac{1}{6}$, 17%

2. $10x$ cm; $6x^2 - 6x$ cm²; $(2x - 2)/(3x + 2)$; 5; 61° 55′ or 56′

3. $\dfrac{3ac + 5b^2}{3bc}$; $\dfrac{3x}{2z} + \dfrac{4y}{5z}$; $\sqrt{\dfrac{y - q}{p}}$; 10; 4, $-2\frac{1}{2}$

4. 128°, 26°, 26°; ADP, BCP; ABP, CDP; 8, 12, 6, 1

5. £5, £4·80

TEST PAPER 3 (page 75)

1. 60; −30; −5, 2, 6; negative

2. $\frac{1}{4}\pi x^2$; $xy - \frac{1}{4}\pi x^2$; $\frac{1}{2}\pi x$; 13·4 cm; 11 cm

3. $\frac{1}{7}$; 255; 26·40, 0·01716, 0·4818; 58° 20′, 0·5250, 1·6212

4. 875; £1 800, £1 200, £3 000; £270, £675

5. 1·46 cm

TEST PAPER 4 (page 76)

1. $4x$; $x^2(x^2 - 4)$; $\dfrac{2}{x^2 - 4}$; x^2; 0, −2; 2, −2; $0 < x < 2$

2. 4h 10 min; 72 km/h; £2·02½; 90 cm³/km

3. 52°, 64°, 90°, 116°; 8·99 cm, 4·38 cm; 19·7 cm², 3·94 cm

4. 1st. by 50p   **5.** 21 cm; 1 410 l

TEST PAPER 5 (page 77)

1. $7x$, $2x^2 - x - 6$, $x + 5$; $\frac{1}{2}(a - 3)$; $2b + 7$; $-\frac{4}{5}$

2. £108; 0·4170, 179·9; $3\frac{1}{2}$, −4; 10, 126°

3. 120 cm³; 168 cm²; 11·18 cm; 53° 8′; 5, 80 cm³

4. £4·30; £48·96; £42·50

5. 25·6 naut. ml.; 11·3 naut. ml.; S. 66° 14′ (or 15′) E.

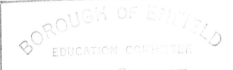